W9-BWJ-522

RAISINS AND ALMONDS

Raisins and Almonds

Fredelle Bruser Maynard

DOUBLEDAY CANADA LIMITED, TORONTO, ONTARIO

DOUBLEDAY & COMPANY, INC., GARDEN CITY, NEW YORK

1972

Some of these stories first appeared in Good Housekeeping, The Kenyon Review, *and* The Malahat Review.

818.5
M

Library of Congress Catalog Card Number 78–176349
Copyright 1964, 1967, 1968, 1972 by Fredelle Bruser Maynard
All Rights Reserved
Printed in the United States of America
First Edition

*To my mother
and
the memory of my father*

Acknowledgments

I am grateful to the many individuals, institutions, and foundations whose support over the years made possible my continued education and growth. In particular I would mention James E. Richardson of Winnipeg, donor of the scholarships which assisted so many of my contemporaries at the University of Manitoba; the Canadian Federation of University Women, which financed much of my graduate education; and the Radcliffe Institute, under whose generous auspices I wrote this book.

Under Freidele's little bed,
A white goat lays his silken head.
The goat goes tripping down the street
To buy raisins and almonds for my sweet.
Raisins and almonds are tasty food,
Freidele will be healthy and good.
Goodness and health are the best things to own,
Freidele will read Torah when she is grown.
                              —Yiddish Cradle Song

CONTENTS

RAISINS AND ALMONDS

COYOTES AND
GRAIN ELEVATORS

⸺•⸺

THAT DAY the first man walked the moon, I thought, "I must be older than I am." I have known forests where no tree was ever cut, land never seeded by hand, and a world where nature was master, not servant, of man. In my world a family's fate hung upon a drought, a blizzard, a hailstorm, a prairie fire; you could work all year and be wiped out in a day. I have drawn water from wells and seen a wildcat outside my window. I remember the first airplane, our first electric light, the phonograph with wooden needles and trumpet horn, and the way sparks flew and sang, steel blue, when the blacksmith shod a horse. I lived on a plain where, only thirty years before, the bison thundered, separated by less than two decades from the ordeal of the Barr colonists—canvas tents in sixty below zero weather, a diet of bannock and gruel. All around me, when I was a child, men broke the land under the fierce promise of the Homestead Act—a quarter section free if within three years you could plow the prairie, raise house and barn, and survive. It can never come again, that free wild perilous world. No one who has known it would willingly return. No one who has left it can forget.

Once I woke on a winter night to a strange sound, a shrill wailing cry, mournful and weird. The window panes were frosted with ice ferns. I melted a peephole with my

finger and looked out. There in the gleaming snow a group
of coyotes, muzzles to the sky, howled the moon.

Birch Hills was two streets, a line of grain elevators, and
a railway station. Not that I saw it so during the years
I lived there. I was three when we arrived, nine when
we moved away. We passed through many small towns afterwards, but Birch Hills has remained for me always The
Town, the essential prairie experience. I can walk in my
mind every foot of its wooden sidewalks, move through the
rooms of our small brown house there as familiarly as if
I had never left. Looking back, I am astonished to realize
its cramping limitations. (My children would say, "What
could you *do* in a place like that?") Yet though often lonely
I was never, I think, bored. Bounded in a nutshell, I
counted myself king of infinite space.

Strung out along Main Street (one could hardly call it
"downtown") were four false-fronted general stores—rather
a lot for a village whose population cannot have been more
than five hundred. One Frenchman, one Scot, one Norwegian, and one Jew—my father. I remember them that way
because that was their meaning in 1925. Only the Norwegian
prospered. There was a fascinating butcher shop, sawdust-
floored, where whole sides of beef and pork hung from great
ceiling hooks. In the barbershop, Sammy Horton's father
sheared creamy froth off rough cheeks with a straight razor.
Children didn't much go to barbershops; a familiar billboard
of the time, advertising cooking fat, showed a boy with an
inverted lard pail on his head, his mother solemnly cutting
round its edge. The legend: *Domestic Shortening.* We had a
cafe (pronounced to rhyme with *safe*), a blockish-looking

bank, the town's only brick building, and a bakery that smelled in all seasons of moist heat, yeast, and flour.

On the border line between Commerce and Sin stood the hotel, which I was forbidden to enter even when, briefly, I had a friend who lived with her proprietor parents in one of its dingy rooms. The hotel's chief *raison d'être* was its beer parlor. Certainly it entertained no "guests" in the usual sense of that word, though salesmen alighted there on their way to other, equally dreary spots. (Thinking of those salesmen revives for me a sense of the town's isolation. They were always called *travelers*. Not even commercial travelers, just travelers. And when my father brought one home for dinner, Mama set out the good china. On such occasions we were likely to have waffles, a sophisticated food appropriate to worldly visitors.) The hotel also provided a meeting corner for local disreputables. Any hour of the day, in good weather, men lounged on a narrow bench by its front door. Joe Breen, a half-breed with a taste for hair tonic; old Ellis, who was not really old but bent over and dull-eyed from sleeping sickness; Doc Bender, surely not a medical doctor, reputed to know all about phrenology and to give head-bump readings in the hotel's back parlor for a quarter; a huddle of farmers' sons, in for the day while their fathers unloaded wheat at the elevators. We always walked fast when we went by the hotel.

It is strange to recollect that our town had no policeman. Such trouble as occurred—a drunk on the rampage, somebody's wife "gone crazy"—would be dealt with by the Mounties, the red-coated members of the Royal Canadian Mounted Police. A Mountie's riding into town was an event. So was the occasional appearance of a wandering contingent of Salvation Army members, the women plain and lofty countenanced in their hard blue bonnets, the men a trifle seedy, making up on a rolling drum what they lacked in presence. Once, when the Army came, I disgraced myself terribly. They had been putting on a good show, those soldiers of the Lord, shaking their tambourines mightily and singing the risen Christ. But the response, in a devout Lutheran community, was embarrassingly lukewarm. When, at the climax of the street-corner service, the sergeant-major boomed out, "Who will COME and be WASHED in the BLOOD of the LAMB?" no one stepped forward. There was a long, awkward silence. He tried again, this time supported by a wail of women. Again, nothing. A reckless sense of social obligation overcame my normal shyness. I stepped forth, the only Jewish child in town, and presented myself for baptism.

Though we had a doctor in Birch Hills, his function was pretty much confined to delivering babies and making the diagnoses which resulted in the dread QUARANTINE signs being nailed to one's door. I suppose, given our lonely situation and the primitive pharmacology of the twenties, there wasn't much a general practitioner could do except sit by bedsides looking grave or wise. Minor illnesses were treated by mothers in accordance with generally esteemed folk practice. Most cures began with enemas or castor oil. The standard treatment for earache, I remember, was pouring hot melted butter into the ear. Tooth troubles meant oil of clove. If that failed, you tied a string to the aching tooth, attached the other end of the string to a doorknob— and slammed the door. The common cold, and all related afflictions, evoked an extraordinary range of comforts. In our house, at the first cough, we were put to bed under quilts and fed hot milk and honey. If the cough "developed," our chests were swathed in mustard plasters made from out-grown woolen underwear, very cheering. An aggravated condition called for the building of a bed tent. Then heavy blankets, supported by the bedposts, enclosed the patient in warm fragrant dark while heated eucalyptus and friar's balsam gave off their curative steams. This experience was especially pleasant if you could hear the wind howling out-side and be assured, by ambulatory members of the family, that the thermometer registered fifty below.

Birch Hills had already a theater in those days. For ten cents on Saturday night you could see Lon Chaney in *The Hunchback of Notre Dame* or Colleen Moore in an orange blossom romance. There was no sound track, of course, but the local pianist thumped away in the dark, suiting her chords to the crash of a plane (*Wings*) or that thrilling moment at the end of a cowboy picture when Hoot Gibson leaned towards his lady love and held his hat before their canted lips. Occasionally we had live entertainment, a vaudeville road show. My chief memory here is of talcum-powdered limbs in pale mauve light and blackface dancers with wide watermelon mouths. Striped trousers, twirling canes, much eye rolling and finger snapping . . .

Once every summer Chautauqua rolled into town, a great event that began with a community parade (I and my friends wearing curtains) and ended in an evening's drama under the big tent. Years later, I was surprised to discover Chautauqua's connection with the temperance movement. So *that* was the meaning of those long dull speeches! To my family the occasion signified uplift of another sort—Cul-ture, the Arts. Middle-aged ladies with wonderful bosoms sang "The Last Rose of Summer" or struck tragic poses to declaim, "Curfew *shall not* ring tonight!" Afterwards Mama

always invited the chief performers to dinner at our house—
as she invited teachers, book salesmen, anyone who might
conceivably touch her children's lives with the magic of
learning. I see them now around our dining room table,
recognizing, with the perspective of distance, people who
in another decade would parade their fragile talents on
Major Bowes' Amateur Hour. They ate a great deal, those
elocutionists. (Once, slipping a sticky pecan bun into her
dress pocket, a maiden guest caught my astonished eye and
murmured, "I can't make them this good at home.") Dinner
over, we retired—three steps away—to the living room, where
my sister played piano and I recited. At seven or eight I
had already a considerable repertoire, ranging from Byron's
invocation to the waves ("Roll on, thou deep and dark blue
ocean, roll!") to a broken doll lament beginning, "I've got
a pain in my sawdust." For a Chautauqua audience I usually
rendered something grand, like *Spartacus to the Gladiators
at Capua*. After the spattered applause came the moment
for which everything else had been so devotedly prepared—
the yolk-yellow soup, delicate *gefilte* fish, the roast chicken
and potatoes, and maids-of-honor tarts with caps of
whipped cream. . . . "Do you think," Mama asked, "Freidele has a future?" They always answered *Yes*.

For the most part, in Birch Hills, we made our own entertainment. The Masonic Lodge, the town's noblest organ-
ization, held an annual Children's Night and a summer pic-
nic. (It is strange to recall now the near reverence with
which my father viewed the Masons. Individually he recognized them as ordinary fellows, but when they gathered in
their blue aprons they took on mystic significance. His elec-
tion to the Order was a great, an unlooked-for triumph.
"When I die," he said, "you should remember to lay be-

side me the Masonic apron.") The school had special events too. My favorite was Sports Day, when we exhibited the now vanished skills of Indian Clubs and something called Grecian Friezes. (Wearing floor-length costumes of sleazy rayon satin, we struck attitudes vaguely suggesting Doric nobility.)

The most ambitious entertainments were church-sponsored. No one seemed to mind that the offerings at church concerts were repetitive. Hazel Morse always sang "Little Brown Jug," Olaf Swenson did his Al Jolson imitation, my best friend Fern tapped out a precisely measured dance to "The Sidewalks of New York." Because I had taken elocution lessons with a real teacher in Winnipeg I knew more "pieces" than most, but audiences were so familiar with my material that they could—and did—correct me when I left out a verse of *The Little Sugar Pig*. The church also arranged events where the chief activity seemed to be eating. (I recall distinctly the exciting and most unchurchlike atmosphere of a box lunch social, where young women, giggling and blushing, were auctioned off along with their cucumber sandwiches.) Though we, as Jews, had no church connections, my mother contributed generously to the pastry tables. This was partly business, I suppose—a way of creating goodwill among customers. But it was also, I see now, a gesture towards some sort of communal life and understanding. Would my mother have admitted this? I think not. Her pride, she would have said, dictated the offerings as an expression—oblique but unmistakable—of family style. Nobody baked like my mother. Other women brought flat pale sugar cookies and cakes dampish like mashed potatoes; Mama produced meringues the color of toasted almonds, crumbly rich shortbreads, pillows of puff paste dusted with

sugar, tortes layered with nut creams and Turkish delight.
The Ladies Aid ladies collected recipes for these marvels,
then, over the store counter, reported puzzling failures. "A
cup chopped dates?" Mama would check. "Well—I used
raisins." "And butter?" "Oh, Mrs. Bruser, butter's very dear.
I cook on lard." For apricot and cherry jam, dried apples;
for nuts, puffed wheat. . . . Mama took to turning aside re-
quests for recipes, saying, "Really, I don't measure"—which
was true. To us she shrugged, "So what is the use? The
feeling they don't have." When she tasted any food that
lacked flavor she would say, "*A goyish tam,*" a gentile taste.

In Birch Hills, "the church" meant the Lutheran church,
to which most townspeople belonged. But there was also an
Anglican church, attended by English families, and—meeting in an ordinary house—a congregation notorious for its
unseemly fervor. I suppose they may have been Baptists or
Jehovah's Witnesses. We called them the Holy Rollers, and
I had delicious fantasies of the members, some far too old
and portly for such sports, barreling about the aisles. Apart
from us, I didn't know a single non-church family. Fern
and her parents attended morning *and* evening service, so
Sunday was a lonely day for me. (It was Fern who told
me, sternly, "God doesn't like people to cut paper dolls on
Sunday." Even then, it seemed to me a trivial detail for
God to worry His head about.) I began to pester my father
for something special *we* could do on the Lord's day, and
finally he sent away to a Winnipeg rabbi for a set of
Sunday school leaflets. For a while I was distinctly interested—particularly since the Old Testament stories suggested the attractive possibility of miracles as a shortcut to
things desired. When I came upon the story of Moses at
the battle of Rephidim, I felt as if I had found the philos-

opher's stone. All one had to do, apparently, was hold the arms high and pray. I started at once. Every night I knelt by my bedroom window, raised my arms as high as possible, and kept them there until they ached, praying silently all the while, "Please, God, let me come first in class." It worked. I came first month after month and was, I suppose, well on my way to faith when the devil whispered in my ear. Why not see what I could do on my own? That month I omitted the raised-arm routine entirely—and still headed the class. I threw away the pamphlets.

Life in Birch Hills had a curiously static quality. Few people owned cars. Travel was by horse and buggy in summer, by sleigh in winter. Small children were pulled about snowy streets on sleds with high sides. One of my earliest memories is of lying back in just such a sled, snug under a white bearskin robe, observing the comfortable bulk of my father's back and hearing him whistle an old Low German courting song whose faintly salacious words I learned years later. *"Een oude paar ossen gevlekte koe, Gaf my myn vader wanneer ik vryen doe . . ."* (An old pair of oxen and a speckled cow, My father will give me when I go courting . . .) When I was five—that would have been 1927, the year Lindy flew the Atlantic—we heard, what dazzlement, a plane overhead, and everyone tumbled out to see it slice the sky. But for the most part I had no experience of speed, and little sense of a world beyond. Sometimes beggars came to our door (we called them hoboes), and often, often, as the freight trains shunted through town, I saw huddles of ragged dirty men riding on top or peering out half-open doors. I had heard of gypsies, too—and how you had to watch your clotheslines when their caravans passed by. So I knew there was something besides our town. But my sense

of place was vague indeed. Had I been asked to produce
a Child's Own Geography, it would have gone something
like this. Birch Hills, center. A long car ride away, Round
Lake, where we waded in bathing dresses, and—farther
still—Watrous, a beach for sick people. To the north, Prince
Albert, its special distinction being Woolworth's, really a
fifteen cent store in those days. To the west, Battleford,
where crazy people were locked up. And to the east Winnipeg, the great city, grandparents, *our people*.

I thought our house in Birch Hills rather grand and
perhaps by local standards it was. Some of my friends had
dirt-floor kitchens and walls thickly wadded with newspapers to keep out the cold. We rented a proper house
with front and back yard, an ornate wire fence all around,
and a gate you could swing on. Small details stand out in
my memory as evidence of what would now be called status.
Our front walk was cement, not wood, and bordered in
summer by airy candytuft drifts. We had a substantial veranda, overhung with cucumber vines. (You could burst the
prickly green globes between finger and thumb to produce
a soapy liquid and broad, smooth seeds.) We had our own
ice house, filled every winter with great blocks cut from
the frozen lakes. On the hottest summer days, you could
poke in the damp sawdust and hit cold. We even had a
playhouse, with shelves for doll dishes and wicker furniture
sent by my grandfather.

Inside, our house struck two dominant notes—gentility
(the Jewish *eydelkayt*) and comfort. Gentility was represented by the phonograph, a hand-wound affair on which
we played "Darktown Strutters Ball" and Caruso arias, and
the piano plus metronome. I much preferred the metronome
to the piano, but was willing to play one in order to use

the other. On the walls we displayed real pictures. (I knew many homes whose chief ornament was a calendar of a type I have never seen since. The scene, usually a landscape, was embossed and thickly encrusted, all over, with a glitter material that looked like coarse salt.) We were specially proud of two etchings, brought from "the old country" and presented to us by the Neatbys, an English family my parents admired and trusted because they were *educated*. Another elegance, in my parents' bedroom, was an ivory dressing table set including marvelous objects like a hair receiver (for combings) and the chamois buffer that gave my mother's fingernails their luminous sheen. Such possessions told me—told, I thought, the world—that though we might be poor we were not common, *prost*.

Every room in that long-ago house had its unique feature—my bedroom, an iron-grilled air register through which one could look at the parlor below; the parlor, where a globe of cranberry-colored liquid hung suspended from a metal frame (a salesman had persuaded my father it would extinguish any fire, regardless of size or origin); the dining room, with a trap door that led to the fruit cellar and furnace. But the heart of the house was its kitchen. Here stood the black iron stove and its many comforts—the reservoir that held hot water for washing up; the warming oven, at all times full of crisp cinnamon toast; and, pushed to the back of the range, a kettle of steaming soup or a pot of porridge with brown sugar. Some people had only an outdoor pump, but we had one right in the kitchen. That was for "regular" water. Drinking water we made from ice in a cooler; soft water, for washing one's hair, came from the rain barrel outside. The notion of a tap from which all-purpose water flowed would have struck me as extraordinary. So, when I first heard of it, did the notion of pressing a button to produce light. We carried kerosene lamps from room to room; when, towards the end of our stay in Birch Hills, our house was wired for electricity, I quite missed the smell of coal oil and the endless mystery of the blue-burning wicks.

How did we amuse ourselves without radio or TV or elaborate toys? Even books were scarce. Our family collection consisted mostly of Yiddish and Hebrew volumes. We owned a complete O. Henry, a frightening autobiography called *I Married A Gentile,* and one novel, distributed free of charge by a clothing firm, called *Skinner's Dress Suit.* Few classics have left on me a more enduring impression than that tale of a poor young man who rises rapidly through the ranks after he purchases a suit from the Tip Top Tailors. It introduced me to two ideas—the scarcity of Great Auks ("Skinner," says the grim-faced employer in Chapter One, "a raise in this business is rare as the Great Auk"), and the impression that virtue is all very well, but it's tailoring that counts. Over the years I acquired a few books of my own and read them over and over: a clutch of *Littles* (*Little Lord Fauntleroy, Little Women, The Little Lame Prince*), *Black Beauty, Grimm's Fairy Tales.* (I can't say "The Snow Queen" was my *favorite.* How can one "like best" so terrible a tale? But its extraordinary blend of beauty, cruelty and deadly cold enchanted me.) For the rest—my father habitually asked customers, "You have books, yes?" I read whatever they had and would lend. I went through all of Dickens that way, breathlessly, because the set belonged to the preacher and there was a chance he might move to another parish before I reached *Hard Times.* Sometimes, at Christmas, I got *Blackie's Annual,* a fat compendium of stories and jokes. The jokes were on the order of "Weather Report: Look out the window and see if it's raining"; the stories frequently involved unknown historical events, so their meaning remained opaque to me. I remember puzzling over one, with illustration of a vaudeville "darky" and the punch line, "I'se free, Massa, I'se free!" Since I had never heard of the slavery, let alone the emancipation of American Negroes, I thought that a pointless tale.

Indoors, we played paper dolls and cards, or rummaged through the attic for dress-up costumes. Outdoors, our games ran the cycle of the seasons. Winter was skating, sledding, building snow houses or watching adult games, hockey and curling. (I once read that hockey is the truly Canadian game, played as it is "on our great universal, ice," and simulating the destructive forces of nature. For me it is curling that seems most Canadian, or at least closest to the rhythm of the life I knew. Curling is laborious, stolid, leaden-gray and oddly domestic, as much broom-centered as rock-centered.) In April, when ice cracked and snow melted, we moved on to marbles, skipping, and hopscotch. A good India rubber ball was important for summer, either to bounce on the sidewalk ("One, two, three a-lairy, I saw Mistress Mary . . .") or to bat against a wall. Bicycles were rare, tricycles nonexistent. The big thing was to have a wagon for pulling and—much more exciting—whizzing about the sidewalks, with the handle bent back to steer, one knee on the seat, and one rapid foot scuffing the ground. I had a metal hoop and stick once, but that was something of an anachronism. Most of my friends owned a pair of homemade stilts and a butterfly net for chasing the great black and gold Monarchs that massed thick as buttercups.

The only widely used "boughten" toy I remember was the Yo-Yo, which hit the prairies around 1930 like a hailstorm. Just picking flowers was a diversion, from furry spring crocus to the last dusty goldenrod. We gathered berries of all sorts—chokecherries that puckered the mouth, raspberries, hairy gooseberries, saskatoons. Rounded up in groups, we played Statues, Peggy, Follow the Leader, Giant Steps or London Bridge (which I called London *Bridges* from its supposed first line, "London Bridges falling down. . . .").

Summer evenings, so far north, were late bright. You could race out after supper any night and find a gang ready to play. In the brief democracy of those waning hours, children of all ages joined in; it was the best moment for team games. That is how I see Birch Hills now, in dusky lavender light. We have gathered in the field by the skating rink; the town lies behind us, the woods thicken round. I smell crushed grass and clover and—from a nearby garden, heavy, sickish-sweet—the white night-blooming tobacco plant. Fireflies wink and fade. Someone calls, "Run! Quick!" All the others have made it, across a dangerous no-man's-land, to the safety of goal, and in the sudden dark I hear the leader's cry:

> "Red Rover, Red Rover,
> I call Freidele over."

JEWISH CHRISTMAS

CHRISTMAS, when I was young, was the season of bitterness. Lights beckoned and tinsel shone, store windows glowed with mysterious promise, but I knew the brilliance was not for me. Being Jewish, I had long grown accustomed to isolation and difference. Difference was in my bones and blood, and in the pattern of my separate life. My parents were conspicuously unlike other children's parents in our predominantly Norwegian community. Where my schoolmates were surrounded by blond giants appropriate to a village called Birch Hills, my family suggested still the Russian plains from which they had emigrated years before. My handsome father was a big man, but big without any suggestion of physical strength or agility; one could not imagine him at the wheel of a tractor. In a town that was all wheat and cattle, he seemed the one man wholly devoted to urban pursuits: he operated a general store. Instead of the native costume—overalls and mackinaws—he wore city suits and pearl-gray spats. In winter he was splendid in a plushy chinchilla coat with velvet collar, his black curly hair an extension of the high Astrakhan hat which he had brought from the Ukraine. I was proud of his good looks, and yet uneasy about their distinctly oriental flavor.

My mother's difference was of another sort. Her beauty was not so much foreign as timeless. My friends had slender young Scandinavian mothers, light of foot and blue of eye; my mother was short and heavyset, but with a face of classic proportions. Years later I found her in the portraits of Ingres and Corot—face a delicate oval, brown velvet eyes, brown silk hair centrally parted and drawn back in a lustrous coil—but in those days I saw only that she too was different. As for my grandparents, they were utterly unlike the benevolent, apple-cheeked characters who presided over happy families in my favorite stories. (Evidently all those happy families were gentile.) My grandmother had no fringed shawl, no steel-rimmed glasses. (She read, if at all, with the help of a magnifying glass from Woolworth's.) Ignorant, apparently, of her natural role as gentle occupant of the rocking chair, she was ignorant too of the world outside her apartment in remote Winnipeg. She had brought Odessa with her, and—on my rare visits—she smiled lovingly, uncomprehendingly, across an ocean of time and space. Even more unreal was my grandfather, a black cap and a long beard bent over the Talmud. I felt for him a kind of amused tenderness, but I was glad that my schoolmates could not see him.

At home we spoke another language—Yiddish or Russian—and ate rich foods whose spicy odors bore no resemblance to the neighbor's cooking. We did not go to church or belong to clubs or, it seemed, take any meaningful part in the life of the town. Our social roots went, not down into the foreign soil on which fate had deposited us, but outwards, in delicate, sensitive connections, to other Jewish families in other lonely prairie towns. Sundays, they congregated around our table, these strangers who were brothers; I saw that they too ate knishes and spoke with faintly foreign voices, but I could not feel for them or for their

silent swarthy children the kinship I knew I owed to all
those who had been, like us, both chosen and abandoned.

All year I walked in the shadow of difference; but at
Christmas above all, I tasted it sour on my tongue. There
was no room at the tree. "You have Hanukkah," my father
reminded me. "That is *our* holiday." I knew the story, of
course—how, over two thousand years ago, my people had
triumphed over the enemies of their faith, and how a single
jar of holy oil had miraculously burned eight days and
nights in the temple of the Lord. I thought of my father
lighting each night another candle in the *menorah,* my
mother and I beside him as he recited the ancient prayer:
"Blessed art Thou, O Lord our God, ruler of the universe,
who has sanctified us by thy commandments and com-
manded us to kindle the light of Hanukkah." Yes, we had
our miracle too. But how could it stand against the glamor
of Christmas? What was *gelt,* the traditional gift coins, to
a sled packed with surprises? What was Judas Maccabaeus
the liberator compared with the Christ child in the manger?
To my sense of exclusion was added a sense of shame.
"You *killed* Christ!" said the boys on the playground. "*You*
killed him!" I knew none of the facts behind this awful
accusation, but I was afraid to ask. I was even afraid to
raise my voice in the chorus of "Come All Ye Faithful"
lest I be struck down for my unfaithfulness by my own
God, the wrathful Jehovah. With all the passion of my
child's heart I longed for a younger, more compassionate
deity with flowing robe and silken hair. Reluctant conscript
to a doomed army, I longed to change sides. I longed for
Christmas.

Although my father was in all things else the soul of
indulgence, in this one matter he stood firm as Moses. "You

cannot have a tree, *herzele*. You shouldn't even want to sing the carols. You are a Jew." I turned the words over in my mind and on my tongue. What was it, to be a Jew in Birch Hills, Saskatchewan? Though my father spoke of Jewishness as a special distinction, as far as I could see it was an inheritance without a kingdom, a check on a bank that had failed. Being Jewish was mostly not doing things other people did—not eating pork, not going to Sunday school, not entering, even playfully, into childhood romances, because the only boys around were *goyishe* boys. I remember, when I was five or six, falling in love with Edward Prince of Wales. Of the many arguments with which Mama might have dampened my ardor, she chose surely the most extraordinary. "You can't marry him. He isn't Jewish." And of course, finally, definitely, most crushing of all, being Jewish meant not celebrating Christ's birth. My parents allowed me to attend Christmas parties, but they made it clear that I must receive no gifts. How I envied the white and gold Norwegians! Their Lutheran church was not glamorous, but it was less frighteningly strange than the synagogue I had visited in Winnipeg, and in the Lutheran church, each December, joy came upon the midnight clear.

It was the Lutheran church and its annual concert which brought me closest to Christmas. Here there was always a tree, a jolly Santa Claus, and a program of songs and recitations. As the town's most accomplished elocutionist, I was regularly invited to perform. Usually my offering was comic or purely secular—*Santa's Mistake, The Night Before Christmas*, a scene from *A Christmas Carol*. But I had also memorized for such occasions a sweetly pious narrative about the housewife who, blindly absorbed in cleaning her house for the Lord's arrival, turns away a beggar and finds she has rebuffed the Savior himself. Oddly enough, my recital of this vitally un-Jewish material gave my parents no pain. My father, indeed, kept in his safe-deposit box along with other valuables a letter in which the Lutheran minister spoke gratefully of my last Christmas performance. "Through her great gift, your little Freidele has led many to Jesus." Though Papa seemed untroubled by considerations of whether this was a proper role for a Jewish child, reciting *The Visit* made me profoundly uneasy. And I suppose it was this feeling, combined with a natural disinclination to stand unbidden at the feast, which led me, the year I was seven, to rebel.

We were baking in the steamy kitchen, my mother and I—or rather she was baking while I watched, fascinated as always, the miracle of the strudel. First, the warm ball of dough, no larger than my mother's hand. Slap, punch, bang—again and again she lifted the dough and smacked it down on the board. Then came the moment I loved. Over the kitchen table, obliterating its patterned oilcloth, came a damask cloth; and over this in turn a cloud of flour. Beside it stood my mother, her hair bound in muslin, her hands and arms powdered with flour. She paused a moment. Then, like a dancer about to execute a particularly difficult pirouette, she tossed the dough high in the air, catching it with a little stretching motion and tossing again until the ball was ball no longer but an almost transparent rectangle. The strudel was as large as the tablecloth now. "*Unter Freidele's vigele Ligt eyn groys veys tsigele,*" she sang. "Under Freidele's little bed A white goat lays his silken head." *Tsigele iz geforen handlen Rozinkes mit mandlen. . . .*" For some reason that song, with its gay fantastic images of the white goat shopping for raisins and

almonds, always made me sad. But then my father swung
open the storm door and stood, stamping and jingling his
galoshes buckles, on the icy mat.

"Boris, look how you track in the snow!"

Already flakes and stars were turning into muddy puddles.
Still booted and icy-cheeked he swept us up—a kiss on the
back of Mama's neck, the only spot not dedicated to strudel,
and a hug for me.

"You know what? I have just now seen the preacher.
Reverend Pederson, he wants you should recite at the
Christmas concert."

I bent over the bowl of almonds and snapped the nut-
cracker.

"I should tell him it's all right, you'll speak a piece?"
No answer.

"Sweetheart—dear one—you'll do it?"

Suddenly the words burst out. "No, Papa! I don't want
to!"

My father was astonished. "But why not? What is it with
you?"

"I hate those concerts!" All at once my grievances
swarmed up in an angry cloud. "I never have any fun! And
everybody else gets presents and Santa Claus never calls
out 'Freidele Bruser'! They all know I'm Jewish!"

Papa was incredulous. "But, little daughter, always you've
had a good time! Presents! What presents? A bag of candy,
an orange? Tell me, is there a child in town with such
toys as you have? What should you want with Santa Claus?"

It was true. My friends had tin tea sets and dolls with
sawdust bodies and crude Celluloid smiles. I had an Eaton
Beauty with real hair and delicate jointed body, two French
dolls with rosy bisque faces and—new this last Hanukkah—

Rachel, my baby doll. She was the marvel of the town: exquisite china head, overlarge and shaped like a real infant's, tiny wrinkled hands, legs convincingly bowed. I had a lace and taffeta doll bassinet, a handmade cradle, a full set of rattan doll furniture, a teddy bear from Germany and real porcelain dishes from England. What *did* I want with Santa Claus? I didn't know. I burst into tears.

Papa was frantic now. What was fame and the applause of the Lutherans compared to his child's tears? Still bundled in his overcoat he knelt on the kitchen floor and hugged me to him, rocking and crooning. "Don't cry, my child, don't cry. You don't want to go, you don't have to. I tell them you have a sore throat, you can't come."

"Boris, wait. Listen to me." For the first time since my outburst, Mama spoke. She laid down the rolling pin, draped the strudel dough delicately over the table, and wiped her hands on her apron. "What kind of a fuss? You go or you don't go, it's not such a big thing. But so close to Christmas you shouldn't let them down. The one time we sit with them in the church and such joy you give them. Freidele, look at me. . . ." I snuffled loudly and obeyed, not without some satisfaction in the thought of the pathetic picture I made. "Go this one time, for my sake. You'll see, it won't be so bad. And if you don't like it—pffff, no more! All right? Now, come help with the raisins."

On the night of the concert we gathered in the kitchen again, this time for the ritual of the bath. Papa set up the big tin tub on chairs next to the black iron stove. Then, while he heated pails of water and sloshed them into the tub, Mama set out my clothes. Everything about this moment contrived to make me feel pampered, special. I was lifted in and out of the steamy water, patted dry with thick towels, powdered from neck to toes with Mama's best scented talcum. Then came my "reciting outfit." My friends in Birch Hills had party dresses mail-ordered from Eaton's —crackly taffeta or shiny rayon satin weighted with lace or flounces, and worn with long white stockings drawn up over long woolen underwear. My dress was Mama's own composition, a poem in palest peach crepe de chine created from remnants of her bridal trousseau. Simple and flounce-less, it fell from my shoulders in a myriad of tiny pleats no wider than my thumbnail; on the low-slung sash hung a cluster of silk rosebuds. Regulation drop-seat underwear being unthinkable under such a costume, Mama had devised a snug little apricot chemise which made me, in a world of wool, feel excitingly naked.

When at last I stood on the church dais, the Christmas tree glittering and shimmering behind me, it was with the familiar feeling of strangeness. I looked out over the audi-ence-congregation, grateful for the myopia that made faces indistinguishable, and began:

> A letter came on Christmas morn
> In which the Lord did say
> "Behold my star shines in the east
> And I shall come today.
> Make bright thy hearth. . . ."

The words tripped on without thought or effort. I knew by heart every nuance and gesture, down to the modest curtsey and the properly solemn pace with which I returned to my seat. There I huddled into the lining of Papa's coat, hardly hearing the "Beautiful, beautiful!" which accompanied his hug. For this was the dreaded moment. All around me, children twitched and whispered. Santa had come.

"Olaf Swenson!" Olaf tripped over a row of booted feet, leapt down the aisle and embraced an enormous package. "Ellen Njaa! Fern Dahl! Peter Bjorkstrom!" There was a regular procession now, all jubilant. Everywhere in the hall children laughed, shouted, rejoiced with their friends. "What'd you get?" "Look at mine!" In the seat next to me, Gunnar Olsen ripped through layers of tissue: "I got it! I got it!" His little sister wrestled with the contents of a red net stocking. A tin whistle rolled to my feet and I turned away, ignoring her breathless efforts to retrieve it.

And then—suddenly, incredibly, the miracle came. "Freidele Bruser!" For me, too, the star had shone. I looked up at my mother. A mistake surely. But she smiled and urged me to my feet. "Go on, look, he calls you!" It was true. Santa was actually coming to meet me. My gift, I saw, was not wrapped—and it could be no mistake. It was a doll, a doll just like Rachel, but dressed in christening gown and cap. "Oh Mama, look! He's brought me a doll! A twin for Rachel! She's just the right size for Rachel's clothes. I can take them both for walks in the carriage. They can have matching outfits. . . ." I was in an ecstasy of plans.

Mama did not seem to be listening. She lifted the hem of the gown. "How do you like her dress? Look, see the petticoat?"

"They're beautiful!" I hugged the doll rapturously. "Oh, Mama, I *love* her! I'm going to call her Ingrid. Ingrid and Rachel. . . ."

During the long walk home Mama was strangely quiet. Usually I held my parents' hands and swung between them. But now I stepped carefully, clutching Ingrid.

"You had a good time, yes?" Papa's breath frosted the night.

"Mmmmmmm." I rubbed my warm cheek against Ingrid's cold one. "It was just like a real Christmas. I got the best present of anybody. Look, Papa—did you see Ingrid's funny little cross face? It's just like Rachel's. I can't wait to get her home and see them side by side in the crib."

In the front hall, I shook the snow from Ingrid's lace bonnet. "A hot cup cocoa maybe?" Papa was already taking the milk from the icebox. "No, no, I want to get the twins ready for bed!" I broke from my mother's embrace. The stairs seemed longer than usual. In my arms Ingrid was cold and still, a snow princess. I could dress her in Rachel's flannel gown, that would be the thing. . . . The dolls and animals watched glassy-eyed as I knelt by the cradle. It rocked at my touch, oddly light. I flung back the blankets. Empty. Of course.

Sitting on the cold floor, the doll heavy in my lap, I wept for Christmas. Nothing had changed then, after all. For Jews there was no Santa Claus; I understood that. But my parents. . . . *Why* had they dressed Rachel?

From the kitchen below came the mingled aromas of hot chocolate and buttery popcorn. My mother called softly. "Let them call," I said to Ingrid-Rachel. "I don't care!" The face of the Christmas doll was round and blank under her cap; her dress was wet with my tears. Brushing them away, I heard my father enter the room. He made no move to touch me or lift me up. I turned and saw his face tender and sad like that of a Chagall violinist. "Mama worked every night on the clothes," he said. "Yesterday even, knitting booties."

Stiff-fingered, trembling, I plucked at the sleeve of the christening gown. It was indeed a miracle—a wisp of batiste but as richly overlaid with embroidery as a coronation robe. For the first time I examined Rachel's new clothes—the lace insets and lace overlays, the French knots and scalloped edges, the rows of hemstitching through which tiny ribbons ran like fairy silk. The petticoat was tucked and pleated. Even the little diaper showed an edge of hand crochet. There were booties and mittens and a ravishing cap.

"Freidele, dear one, my heart," my father whispered. "We did not think. We could not know. Mama dressed Rachel in the new clothes, you should be happy with the others. We so much love you."

Outside my window, where the Christmas snow lay deep and crisp and even, I heard the shouts of neighbors returning from the concert. "Joy to the world!" they sang,

> Let earth receive her King!
> Let every heart prepare Him room
> And heaven and nature sing . . .

It seemed to me, at that moment, that I too was a part of the song. I wrapped Rachel warmly in her shawl and took my father's hand.

SATISFACTION GUARANTEED—
THE 1928 EATON'S CATALOGUE

·»·——◄►·◉·◄◉►··◄···

IF ANYONE were to ask what books influenced my child-hood, I wouldn't hesitate. Dickens—thought of as a single, tremendous entity, at once enlarging and illuminating the life of our prairie town; the *Book of Knowledge;* and the T. Eaton Co. catalogue. Perhaps the catalogue seems a curious choice, and yet in its way (which was sociological, not literary) it performed the functions of the other two. Like the *Book of Knowledge,* it was encyclopedic; like Dickens, it brought the world to my door. No one un-familiar with the western plains can conceive of their un-imaginable loneliness—the flat land beneath the bowl of sky. Summers, the endless undulations of wheat fields in a noon haze; winters, the great drifted expanse of furrowed snow . . . a life austere as the grain elevators that stabbed the horizon and fierce as a wildcat's scream. My knowledge of absolutes—all absolutes—is based on that experience. When I first read *Samson Agonistes*—"O dark, dark, dark amid the blaze of noon, Irrecoverably dark, total eclipse Without all hope of day"—blindness pulsed behind my lids because I had known total eclipse: I had lived in Birch Hills, Saskatchewan. Total? Not quite. There were books, evidence of a world beyond. Dickens brought peo-ple; the *Book of Knowledge,* a rich salmagundi of puzzles, projects, information, romantic story; and the catalogue brought me *things*.

There were two issues of Eaton's catalogue—Spring and Summer, Fall and Winter. The fall issue was the important one. It came with goldenrod and the clicking of crickets, with pressing leaves (dun yellow and brown, never the extravagant blaze of eastern maples) and gathering great armfuls of wild purple asters. From early August I watched the post-office boxes until the magic day when every box, almost, showed the transverse line of a package-at-the-wicket card. Then I raced to get Papa so he could dial our box combination. Home with the brown-paper-covered book, I settled in.

There was only one room for catalogue reading—the kitchen—and one place, the kitchen table by the stove. I suppose that is why, when I think now of The Book, I can smell not only its thin browntone paper, but peach halves bubbling in sugar syrup, or the sharp, crisp tang of piccalilli. The taste of the catalogue is the taste of apples cold on the teeth, followed perhaps by a bowl of brazil nuts (which we called nigger toes) or tangerines (which we called Jap oranges). Though for many country families Eaton's was a chief source of goods, in our house the catalogue served no such practical purpose. I don't recall that we ever sent off a single order; our supplies came from Papa's store. The catalogue was a book to dream over, and the fact that I was not getting a new Eaton Beauty doll took nothing from my pleasure in studying her rosy smile and fringy eyelashes. My winter dresses—even my winter coat—would be made by Mama as usual. (Whatever the fashion, I wore variations of her plump-child theme: Peter Pan collar, yoke, and broad straight pleats to disguise a lack of waist.) Still I pored over the city flounces. I read the lists of books and records; even, as the season progressed, the pages of farm supplies. I played "choose-ups" with friends, taking turns at wishing on the catalogue. And when the new copy came—double joy!—I got the old one to cut. (I never saw a commercial paper doll book until I was twelve—and I thought it, then, a sad substitute for Eaton's infinite variety.)

There aren't many copies of the Prairie Bible left. They were cut up, used as bed warmers (nicely toasted in the oven), even—after an elaborate process of page folding—as decorative doorstops. I suppose the great bulk of them ended up in outdoor privies. So it was with a sense of real discovery that I pounced on a copy that turned up not long ago, in the bottom of an old trunk. 1928. The Diamond Jubilee, celebrating Confederation's sixtieth anniversary, had come and gone in a blaze of firecrackers. Mackenzie King was Prime Minister; crops were good; a Dominion-Provincial conference had declared Canada's effective equality with the United Kingdom . . . and Eaton's was selling lamp wick at four cents a yard.

What strikes one first now about the old catalogue is its extraordinary innocence. Nothing even remotely approaches the modern concept of layout or design. Page after page is crowded with painstakingly realistic sketches —ladies in ladies' dresses, children in children's dresses, men in breeches or overalls. One feels, indeed, that the book had no "composer" at all. It is as if some conscientious, unimaginative stock boy had passed along the supply room shelves and dutifully recorded what he found there. Text matches pictures in homely directness. "Good Quality Flat Crepe," "Winter Comfort Assured," "Unusual Value," "For

the Short, Stout Figure." Was ever woman in this manner
wooed? Everywhere, the plain prose emphasizes plainer
virtues. Little is said about style, much about "Cumfy Cut";
what matters is durability, warmth, value-for-the-money.
The housewife who shops these pages does not much care
what everyone else is wearing. She wants to be certain that
what she buys now will be wearable for years to come.
Even moderately frivolous garments are recommended in
terms which emphasize feel, not look: "fleecy, soft nap
makes this dress warm and cosy." Perhaps in the big department stores of Winnipeg and Toronto smart shoppers
asked, "What does Chanel say?" On the prairies, the lead
question was likelier to be "Do the merino combinations
have a closed or open crotch?"

Reading catalogue prose now is a little like sitting down
to a large crockery bowl of old-fashioned porridge. It is
so heavy, so gray, in every way so unpretentious that one
feels the stuff *must* be good. "Here's a misses' extremely
inexpensive dress that adequately meets the exacting needs
of everyday wear during the Fall and Winter. It is fash-
ioned in our factories of durable All-Wool English Crepe
in a straight, simple style, with cosy long set-in sleeves
trimly finished with cuffs. Good satisfaction for such a
small outlay." What is said, what is meant, and what is,
are all very close together here. (The writer is saying, "This
dress is no big thrill, but it will do—and what can you
expect at the price?") The golden age of euphemism has
not dawned in 1928. "Stout" is a common word; so is
"heavy" and "elderly." (The illustrator minces no lines.
Models shown in "approved styles for the larger woman"
are size fifty-twos at least, broad of beam and shoulder and
short of leg.) It is clear, too, that advertising copywriters

have not yet teamed up with the psychologists and motivational researchers. One "Interesting New Style, just the type that attends many happy little informal affairs" is offered in a choice of color combinations—Folly Red with Mother Goose, or Marron Glace with Mother Goose. For those who cannot trust their intuitions, a color table on the front cover provides the necessary clue: Mother Goose is "Medium tan or sand but darker than grain." The color table is a fascinating study in language as well as fashion trends. Very big in fall 1928 were Grasshopper Green, Monkeyskin, and Pinecone ("A medium brown, similar to dead leaves"). There are eight distinct varieties of gray (Battleship, Gull, Zinc, Gunmetal, and so forth), a color called Bran, one called Wigwam, and Drab (really). The liveliest-sounding shades carry dreadfully inappropriate connotations: Grapenuts, Waffle, Muffin ("similar to Toast"). And there is Sedge. A skirt in Sedge, think of it, with Wigwam blouse and hat of Bran.

Occasionally the catalogue attempts loftier flights. Some dresses are "beautiful" and "splendid" as well as "modest in every line." One delicate costume, georgette and velvet, inspires a positively lyrical burst. "A lovely 'dress-up' frock, where Fashion works out her truest art in rich simplicity. No lovelier medium than the rich, softly hanging All-Silk Transparent Velvet, and no lovelier finish than the pretty shoulder flower and the stunning large brilliant clasp that fastens the wide all-around girdle and forms the heading for the soft-swaying flare of the new wrap-around skirt." In a book where the norm is a housedress "of strong, sturdy, wear-resisting Khaki cloth," such prose seems decadent if not downright depraved, and one turns with relief from its oriental seductions to the elemental simplicities of Eaton's

Extra-Large Fleece-Lined Bloomers: "Has roomy gusset and well-sewn seams. Strong, serviceable elastic at waist and knees."

Since the catalogue was primarily a clothing book, it preserves most obviously the fashions of its period, though the image is John Held modified by forty below zero and the McCormick tractor. The women in the flat, stylized illustrations are decidedly on the heavy side, but the heaviness is without any suggestion of sensuous ripeness. They are quite breastless, these large bovine females—and no wonder. The corset pages reveal horrifying Flex O Steel casings "Strongly boned throughout to hold and give the figure a straight line." Back and front laces, inner belts, hooks and clasps and elastic inserts are all calculated to reduce any discrepancy between bust, waist, and hips. For women whose figures resist equalizing, there is a rubber reducing brassiere. Legs, revealed to just knee level, are sexless as sausages. Beneath the neat bobs and cloches, faces are sweetly vacuous, with round eyes, round spots of rouge, and Betty Boop lips accented in bright lipstick. Little girls are miniature adults; the pre-schoolers, with their deep cloche hats and dropped waistlines, look like stout matrons on their way to a Ladies Aid luncheon.

More interesting than fashion data is the evidence, in Eaton's catalogue, of opinion and attitude. Canada in 1928 would seem to have been spectacularly unaware of large elements in its cultural heritage: an "Eskimo doll" is a run-of-the-mill doll in, of all things, a clown suit with pom-poms and ruff at the neck; the "Indian crafts" feature tie holders, score pad covers, and cushion tops all decorated with the identical silhouette of a feathered chieftain (*circa* Tecumseh). As for minority groups other than the indigenous, the Negro appears, predictably, as exotic and ridiculous. A leading fashion color is "Nigger Brown." A featured toy, "Hey, Hey," is a comic-vaudeville representation of a Negro in cheap bright tin. The figure holds a squawking chicken. Wind it up, and "the darkie shuffles along" with his stolen bird, while a small dog, yapping fiercely, attaches itself to the seat of his trousers. Another toy—"very amusing, sure to please"—features two dancing Negroes on a shanty-shaped box from whose windows peer little golliwog children. Again, the theme is See How They Jump.

If the old Eaton's catalogues provide indications of how the prairie farmer saw the rest of the world, they also, of course, reveal what his own world was like. It was *cold*. A sense of winter hardship rises from these pages like frosted breath on a January morning. Oh, there are light-weight church clothes and round-the-house clothes, surely. But the tone of the book is set by all those garments designed for long trudges through the whirling snow, for carrying in wood and carrying out feed to the barn. The children who wore these toques and jumbo sweaters with blanket cloth knickers and lumberjack-style knee stockings were not members of a car pool. If they were lucky, they might ride horseback, or scrunch over snow-packed roads in a horse-drawn sleigh. But mostly they walked—two, three, four miles in forty below weather, with books and a lard pail of lunch. "Here," says the catalogue of a sheepskin-lined model, "is our Sub-Zero coat that we especially offer to the woman who lives on a farm, with a long ride to town . . . or the rural school teacher with a cold walk to school every morning." Even the tams are made of double-knit wool; a page headed "For Days That Are Chilly" features not only the expected mufflers and vests but a variety of cozy garments called hug-me-tights. And the underwear! From this section alone, social historians of the future might reconstruct the image of prairie life before the triumph of electricity and the gasoline engine. Over twenty pages of the 1928 catalogue are devoted to things-to-go-under-things. A few scanties (lustrous sateen bloomers, pongee boudoir caps with insert of satin ribbon), but for the rest, it is woolen all the way. There are shirts and drawers and combinations to enclose every inch of flesh. (The big brand name here, by an odd trick of association, is "Wolsey," every unshrinkable undergarment stamped with the cardinal's noble profile.) There are kneewarmers to go over the underwear and under the overstockings; abdominal protectors ("for maximum comfort and warmth during severe cold weather"); fleece-lined petticoats and knitted underpants. Just reading about these marvels is an experience in ultimate coziness, like sitting by a wood stove on a bitter night.

Precisely because prairie winters were so ferocious, the demands of prairie life so unremitting, farm women craved frivolity. This too Eaton's understood. The hats, for instance, are purest frippery, a tropical paradise of sequins, rhinestones, velvet, feathers, beads. "Pretty Flowers, Ribbons, and Novelties" is a page of baubles for the woman who wore her husband's mackinaw to milk the cows. Here is a crepe de chine hankie, hand-painted. Here is a pair of shirred ribbon garters with rosebud trim, a decorated clothes hanger, a lace collar and cuff set (might perk up those sturdy, low-priced flannel frocks) and even—good heavens! —detachable georgette sleeves and a marabou stole. It must have been a comfort. (Looking at these absurdities, I remember a curiousness that intrigued me as a child. We would visit houses where the living was bare subsistence, all the rooms bleakly practical—and then, in the bedroom, a manifest extravagance—a jewel box of French ivory; a crystal ball that, shaken, drifted artificial snow over an enclosed castle scene; a floppy boudoir doll, satin clad, on the bed. Toys.)

What did people do on those short winter evenings long ago? The catalogue provides clues. They read, by lamplight, Eaton's pocket classics: Edgar Guest, Robert W. Service, a "splendid variety in fiction" including Ethel M. Dell and a host of nameless names. For the children there was matter "clean, interesting, inspiring, educational." (One need not have read *Plain Jane and Pretty Betty* to divine the nature of its clean inspiration.) And, naturally, there was an abundance of home craft supplies. In addition to crochet, knitting, and embroidery, Eaton's offered materials for some justly vanished arts, like painting on oilcloth and creating interesting decorated objects by dipping in a solution of oil and random-mixed color. Those who craved livelier entertainment might provide it themselves. The 1928 book shows only a few gramaphones and radios, but lots of noisemakers—harmonica, accordion, banjo, ukelele, sax. In sheet music, "Honolulu Moon" was big, and the theme song from the talkie *Ramona*. Traditionalists could choose from old reliables like "Mother Machree" and "Love's Old Sweet Song," those standard delights of village concerts.

In sickness as in health, Eaton's stood by its customers. Since farm families had, by and large, to be their own doctors except in real crises, the catalogue offers a dazzling variety of patent medicines. Unlike modern drugs, however, most of which have names that summon up visions of laboratories and faceless scientists, the home remedies

of the twenties are personal. Stomachaches are the province
not of Alka-Seltzer (the name chills), but of Mother Siegel,
whose wise, benign countenance shines forth from every
bottle of curative syrup. For kidney trouble, there is Dr.
A. W. Chase; for blood and nerves, Dr. Williams (Pink
Pills for Pale People). The medical schools of the period
must have worked full time turning out pill vendors. Some,
like the ambitious Dr. Thomas, produced an Eclectric Oil
(not electric, not eclectic) good for all diseases, internal
and external, of horses and men. Sufferers not relieved
by potions could turn, as a last resort, to a twenty-dollar
wonder called the Signal Medical Battery, a Rube Goldberg
construction which employed electric current to cure everything from headache to sore feet. (Accessories included a
plug-in foot plate, a hair brush, two foot sponges, and one
pair of cords. . . .)

The history of mail order in the West is full of drama
—like the single gentleman who tried to order a bride from
the underwear pages, and the townspeople who called their
village "Eatonia" in honor of their patron saint. It is easy
to understand how such things were possible: the catalogue
is a very personal book. A woman in Turtleford or Neepawa,
ordering a bathing suit for her son, would surely feel that
Eaton's *understood.* "Nearly every boy wants a bathing
suit, and at our low price [65¢], there is no reason why
he shouldn't have one. They are light but strongly made
and will stand up under the treatment the ordinary care-
free boy gives a bathing suit." Serious, friendly, sympathetic,
aware, the catalogue writer gives advice on everything from
buttonless combinations ("boys will slip out of it in a
jiffy") to interior decorating. A page of living room furniture includes the reminder that this room is "the heart of

the home. Here the family meets as a family; here social
contact is made with other families and individuals." Even
the order form rises above mere commerce: on the reverse
side, Eaton's offers a thought-provoking essay. "Are You
Getting Ahead? Does money bring happiness? Perhaps not.
Yet money poorly spent can bring unhappiness. . . ." It is,
in short, a dissertation calculated to give prodigals second
thoughts about that new beaded lampshade, and one can
only admire the company's altruism. Readers are encouraged
to send special money problems to the Budget Director,
some of whose sample budgets are printed in the back
pages. (Suggested annual allotment for a farm family of
six with a $2,600 income: $338 for food, $364 for clothing.
"Much depends on home sewing," the Director adds crisply.)
For problems not covered in the body of the book, there
are free pamphlets available. Eaton's Farm News Service
lists titles ranging from "Swat the Fly" to "Helping the
Nervous, Irritable Child."

No wonder farm families waited with such eagerness
for The Book. It was department store, picture magazine
and counseling service rolled into one, a friend in the city
who knew your needs and could be trusted to serve them
with absolute integrity. "Customers reading the 'ads' may
rely upon purchasing merchandise as represented—a spade
is called a spade and not a silvered trowel." Designed for
customers on the remotest farms, without access to stores
of any kind, Eaton's offered a total shopping service. From
the catalogue in 1928 you could order a thimble, a single
pair of shoelaces, a potholder, a dress buckle, a ball of
twine, a collar button. And if you didn't like the thimble
when it arrived, you could return it for prompt, cheerful
refund. Abuses of Eaton's money-back guarantee were

notorious—the dress returned after the dance, the broken toy—and there is just a touch of sad reproach in the catalogue's reminder that return of a used tube of toothpaste "should not be necessary."

Eaton's still serves the western farms, but the catalogue —like the farm—has gone electric. "Walk in," urges the text of a recent edition. "Browse around. There's gear for every kind of action. But beware of the colour explosion. . . . it's deafening! . . . We've picked the ripest plum, the coolest lime. What happened? Pow!" Youth dominates. The catalogue begins with its Junior Shop ("where the gadabout is simply mad-about the pop-in pant suit"), maintains throughout a young, bold, up-to-the-minute stance. Captions are saucy: "My fair mini," "the mocking turtle," "Some like it striped," "A dress for all seasons." Who cares about practicality? "For the Big Freeze" there are sleek stretch pants and fluffy fur hoods. Older women, demoted to mid-book, wear modified junior styles and are elegantly slender. ("Older," like "stout," is a word unheard.) The underwear section is all puffs of lace. Though, presumably, the snows of today are deep as the snows of yesteryear, combinations in the good old Wolsey sense of the word have disappeared. Now there is snappy, with-it ski underwear "available in lightning red." Girdles emphasize ease rather than control; the bones are silent, and stomachs have turned into tummies. Instead of the rubber reducing brassiere, there is a fiberfill padded model which "coaxes you into a fuller roundness." *"You're shaped,"* the New Eaton's croons hypnotically. *"You're slim. You're smooth."*

It's persuasive, the voice of today's Eaton's catalogue— persuasive and lively and various and richly toned. Why then do I miss the shy crudity of that fellow who used to write, with blunt pencil on heavy foolscap, no doubt, those touchingly sincere descriptions? "We feel we are not overestimating its charms when we say this frock looks as though it cost several dollars more than our very moderate price." "You really cannot appreciate what a wonderful value this is unless you have attempted to make yourself a dress out of the same quality fine All-Wool Flannel that we have used here." I miss him and I miss his quality merchandise—the felt shoes and leggings, the driving robes of Chinese dogskin, the Celluloid combs and razor strops and shoe button hooks with mother-of-pearl handles. Where are the wire armbands, the decorated hair receivers, and the smelling salts chunky in cut-glass bottles? Where are the curling tongs and marcel irons, the baby walkers and pen nibs? There's not a plowshare in the book, or a three-ring teat-slitter.

CANDY HEARTS

※→→→●←←←→※

SUMMER in Birch Hills was the lovely season. It was what we waited for, all through the long months when dark came early and the cold shut us indoors by the throbbing stove. May Day brought promise; we raced from door to door with crepe paper candy baskets. Then Victoria Day: we paraded in middies and gym bloomers celebrating, not a long dead queen, but liberation to come. And on the last day of June we burst out the school doors with wild cries of delight.

> No more pencils, no more books,
> No more teachers' dirty looks!

On the first of July, whirling our fizzy sparklers or lighting Roman candles that jetted in the velvet dark, we knew that we were immortal and that summer would never end.

At first no day was quite long enough for all we had to do, Fern and Hazel and I. There was the playhouse to clean up. We stamped the dirt floor till it was smooth as linoleum, scrubbed the shelves and set out the doll dishes. We took down last year's faded brown pictures and tacked up new ones clipped from magazines or old calendars. Sometimes we skipped through the back lanes checking trash barrels for useful oddments, but we gave that up after Fern got a bad cut from the jagged edge of an old

tin can. Mud pies, daisy chains, hopscotch, chokecherries
. . . the days flew past. By the middle of August, we
were seized with a curious mixture of restlessness and bore-
dom. When you came right down to it, what was there,
really, *to do?*

We branched out. "Let's collect rocks," Hazel would say.
Or butterflies, or chips of colored glass. For a while, we
would be fired with competitive excitement. But then,
when the coffee cans were full of specimens, the game
died. "I've got an idea," Hazel said one day. "We can study
bugs."

I rolled over, sucking the moist root of a grass blade.
"Who wants to *study* anything?"

Hazel was already up, dusting off the bottom of her
whoopee pants. "No, look, this'll be fun. Go get your fly
swatter and I'll show you." Kneeling on the cement walk
that led from our front door to the gate, she explained.
"First you kill some flies, see? A lot of them. Then you
lay them on the sidewalk and wait for the ants."

"Will ants really come?" Fern was a doubter.

"Sure—'specially if you squash the fly, so there's blood."
She demonstrated, smashing a large bluebottle so something
thick and white spurted out along with the red.

"It's ugly. Let's play something else." I turned to go, but
Fern called, "Hey, look at *that*, will you? It works!" Sure
enough. A whole army of ants was marching, single file,
heading straight for Hazel's fly. The lead ant circled carefully, feelers quivering. Then the others moved in, pushing,
poking, and tugging. It was like those pictures in the *Book
of Knowledge*, native bearers staggering under the weight
of a dead lion or zebra. Some of the ants stayed behind,
to deal with the white stuff, and when they'd finished,

the sidewalk was clean again. Amazing, really. It was probably educational—and anyway, if I went off by myself, Fern and Hazel would gang up on me. I decided to stay.

I had to be careful, because Fern and Hazel were always putting their heads together. Of course that was natural. Their fathers came from the same town in Norway, and they went to the same church. Everything considered, I was lucky to be included at all. Some of the kids were really mean. (I remember the day we moved to Birch Hills, and the two boys leaned over the fence, gawking. "Is it a nigger?" one asked, staring at my sunburned face. The other shook his head. "Naw. It's a Jew.") But Fern and Hazel weren't like that. Sometimes Hazel's father took me for a ride in their car—I hardly ever got rides—and at Christmas Fern asked me over to see her tree. For my birthday she gave me a picture of herself, sitting with one leg tucked under her accordion-pleated skirt, her doll face lit by a dazzling smile. I admired Hazel, but I loved Fern, and I used to think sometimes that if Hazel moved away, Fern and I could be best friends, just the two of us. I even got Mama to send to Eaton's for a rosewater and glycerine lotion that was supposed to make your skin lighter. (Fern was unbelievably blond.) But I always had the feeling that there was a glass wall between us, and that if I ever forgot, and tried to get through, there would be blood and gashes of broken glass.

We played ants and flies that afternoon until the sun made the cement walk uncomfortable. My bottom felt ridged and prickly. Fern had wandered off and was making whistles out of dandelion stems.

"I'm tired of this." Hazel brought her foot down on a column of ants, scraping it so there was a dry little crunch-

ing noise. "Come on, Fern. Let's go downtown and see
what's doing."

"There won't be nothing doing on a Tuesday afternoon."

"We could go down to the station."

Fern shook her head. "No train today. You know that."

I had a hunch what the next suggestion would be. Hazel
loved playing around the freight cars, swinging up on top
to pretend she was a hobo riding the rails or—horror of
horrors—crawling underneath. No matter how often she
showed me ("See, there isn't any engine, silly! They *can't*
move") I was terribly afraid. Once I did wriggle underneath a car, but when I looked up and saw the machinery,
my ears were suddenly filled with the roar of the trains
and I screamed. So now I spoke quickly. "We could go to
my father's store for bananas."

Hazel groaned. "Oh, horsefeathers. *Bananas.* I mean
something really fun." She thought a minute. "Maybe we
could find Joe Breen."

Joe Breen was the local drunk, a derelict half-breed who
roamed the streets on Saturday nights, loose-eyed and
shambling. He drank hair tonic or vanilla extract, we knew.
That was because Indians couldn't buy real liquor. Fern
and Hazel had made up a special song:

> Joe Breen, In-di-an,
> Drink vanilla if you can.
> If you can't get vanilla,
> Chew an old tin can.

Chanting and hooting joyfully, they would circle around
him. Sometimes they skipped to the tune, blocking his path
with the spinning rope. (Hazel did pepper faster than anybody I knew.)

"You'll never find Joe Breen at this hour," I said.

"Mmmm. Guess not." Suddenly she lit up. "*I've* got it! Let's see if the Chink store's open!"

"The windows are still soaped," I said.

"Yeah, sure. But my ma saw a light in the back. He's there, all right. Bet we could get him to come out."

I felt a delicious chill of excitement. I had never seen a real Chinaman, but of course I knew all about them— how they ate rotten eggs and bandaged their feet and shaved their heads except for a long pigtail that hung down their backs.

"Chinky chinky Chinaman, catch his pig-tail!" Fern sang. "This'll be fun. Say, Hazel . . ." A pause. "D'you think there's China*women* too?"

"Of course, stupid."

"D'you think they—well, *you* know—do the other thing?"

"Like people, you mean?" This was too deep even for Hazel. "How should *I* know? But I bet we can get some free candy."

"We could get candy at our store." I didn't know whether I wanted them to take me up on that or not.

Hazel wasn't listening. She had a plan. "Now when we get there, you bang on the door and tell him to open up, we want to buy some candy, O.K.?"

Fern was puzzled. "I don't have any money. None of us has."

"How's he going to know that, dummy?"

We turned the corner. The windows of the new store *were* still soaped, but the sign was up. "Sunshine Confectionery. Candy, Tobacco, Ice Cream." And—luck was with us—someone was out front sweeping the sidewalk. He wasn't wearing a coolie coat like in the books. That was disappointing. And he had regular hair. But when he raised his head I saw that he was Chinese, all right, a really old-looking Chinese.

Hazel beamed. "Hey, mister, we want to buy some candy."

The man stopped sweeping. When he smiled, his face was crinklier than ever. "Tomorrow. You come tomorrow?" He spoke very slowly and carefully, as if he had to send a bucket down the well for every word.

"No, we want it *now*." She pushed past him and we followed.

"Oh, it's real nice!" Fern said. The store was freshly painted, a pale frosty green like lime sherbet. There was a little round table and chairs with legs like twisted coat hangers, and a long glass counter with bins and bins of candy. My father sold candy, but it was the penny kind or else packaged things—chunky slabs of Mackintosh toffee, Neilson milk chocolate bars, Cracker Jack, boxes of maple buds. This was city candy. "Look, snowballs!" Fern pointed to a bin of fat coconut-covered chocolates. "And jelly babies!"

The man moved behind the counter. He bowed slightly to Hazel. "You show me the kind."

"I don't know, exactly." She cocked her head thoughtfully. "How much raspberry drops would I get for a nickel?"

The man scooped up some raspberry drops and shook them onto the scale. "You see."

"Not enough. How many English toffees for a nickel?" Again he scooped, again she shook her head. She had him weigh up some peanut brittle (he had to crack it with a little silver hammer) and some caramels. Fern joined in. "How many licorice pipes? How many jujubes? How many lemon sours?" The man seemed rattled now. His hands shook ever so slightly as he pattered back and forth to the scale.

He was weighing up lemon sours when Hazel whispered to me. "Tell him you want a dollar's worth of those mints with the printing on them." She pointed at the flat heart-shaped candies, palest mauve and pink and yellow, that said things like "Oh you kid" and "Sweetheart be mine." "Don't be dopey," I whispered back. "He'll know I don't have a dollar!" "For all he knows, you could have a million! You're just scared!" She made a face and moved towards Fern, her corn-silk hair falling in her eyes as she bent over the candy case, tapping. With her cheeks flushed like that, she reminded me of the doll I saw once in Eaton's toy department, that Mama said we couldn't afford. What was the Chinaman to me, anyhow? It was no skin off *my* teeth if he had to weigh up some candy just for exercise. And it wasn't as if we were hurting the old geezer. I spoke very loudly and he looked up, surprised, I guess, because I hadn't said anything before.

"I want a dollar's worth, please. Of the mints."

"You say *one dollar?*" He didn't believe I had a dollar; I knew that. But I knew something else that even Hazel didn't know. He was scared, of us—three little girls with sticky hands. I could have found his wound in any dark. I aimed and struck. "My daddy," I said carefully, "has a big store. And Fern's daddy is the preacher."

For a minute nobody moved. Nobody said anything. I edged closer to Hazel. Then the man smiled. It wasn't like the way he smiled when he saw us for the first time. This was an old wide crumpled smile, pale as a moth's wing. As if we weren't strangers after all, but people he knew very well. He shoveled the mints onto the scale—a candy mountain. I watched the indicator needle dart and flicker. Then, quick as a garter snake's tongue, Hazel leaned forward. "How much are *those?*" Her hand shot out, pointing. I saw her make a fist and bang up, hard, under the little silver cradle of the scale. The candy seemed to explode before our eyes; the pile shot upwards like a firecracker, a fountain of blue and pink and showering yellow. "Cheese it!" Hazel called. She streaked for the door, with Fern at her heels. I heard the small pop and crunch of spattered mints under my shoes as I raced after her, down Main Street, past the hotel and through the alley to Fern's back yard. We collapsed in a heap against the door of the privy, sweating and breathing hard. Hazel's eyes shone. "Did you see the look on the Chink's face? Boy oh boy, that was some fun!"

"I'm thirsty," I said. "I'm going home."

"You can have lemonade at our house." Hazel put one arm around me and one around Fern. We moved down the street, locked together. "Want to write in my autograph book?"

Sitting on Hazel's piazza in the soft blue haze of that summer afternoon, we signed her album. Fern took a popsicle pink page and wrote

> My love is a cabbage
> Divided in two.
> The leaves I give others,
> The heart I give you.

I started the next page but couldn't think of a verse, so I just wrote "Yours till the cellar stairs." When Fern asked why I didn't finish my lemonade, I told her I had a cramp and she nodded. "It comes from running."

But I knew better. Even when I sat perfectly still I felt it—the needle of glass that pierced my heart.

TO WALK THE
GOLDEN STREETS

···•—————•>•<•———•···

MANY CHILDREN grow up, I suppose, not knowing how
their fathers spend the hours between breakfast and dinner.
For me, from the beginning, Papa's store was a central fact
of existence, not only our living but our life. The store
defined our position in the community (substantial though
not rich, and faintly suspect because we dealt in money).
It also defined my father—set off, in a highly visible way,
his personal qualities and his business gifts. He was not
good at making money. What he loved was planning, or-
ganizing, displaying, talking to customers. Every store he
had—and there were many, a steady rhythm of grand openings and bankruptcies—was a marvelously ordered world.
At a time when country store windows went in heavily
for stacked cans of tomato soup, Papa was an artist. Fans
of orange crepe paper, gorgeously pinched and pleated,
flared across the window rear. Twisted green streamers spun
from one corner to the other, and white crepe rosettes lay
scattered about like giant snowflakes, their delicate petals
emphasizing the splendor of a fur hat, the softness of a
glove. At Easter, when the Saskatchewan prairies were still
locked in snow, Papa banked his window with Mother's
ferns and begonias, trundled from home on the rackety store
wagon. (Our old red wagon, painted and with built-up
sides, doubled as delivery truck.) In September, the cozi-

ness of his windows made one positively long for cold: there were puffy quilts, Dr. Denton sleepers the color of porridge, brilliant red scarves, bulky toques, mittens and sleds and stiff heavy coats made of Hudson's Bay blankets. Come Christmas, the town children pressed against the glass, their fingers and steamy breaths leaving patterns of wonder. Here dolls, almost life size, sat around a table spread with Mama's own hand-embroidered linen. Some held dainty porcelain cups to parted lips; others leaned stiffly forward, eyes fixed on a bowl of nuts or a plate of shiny looped ribbon candy. In the corner, a group of friendly animals bent over a toy train; a teddy bear—what deep plush, what lambent eyes!—embraced a duck. There were no price tags. The window sang not "Buy!" but "Enjoy!"

Although almost all of Papa's stores failed miserably, each carried a name that was at once talisman and hope: *The O-Kay Store*. Papa liked the bright, modern-sounding effect of that, but I always preferred the simple legend at the bottom of his sign: B. Bruser, General Merchant. Because Papa was not an ordinary storekeeper. He was a merchant prince, and his store was Ali Baba's cave.

There was no notion, in those days, that a store should be open, airy, brightly colored, agleam with chrome, or that the customer should serve himself. Entering, you moved from prairie sun or prairie wind into a world where the floors were oiled, the walls a heavy dark oak, and the ceiling an extraordinary canopy of raised and patterned metal painted a dull bronze. My favorite department was Ladies Wear, especially fabrics, always referred to as "dry goods." This term, like others in the store, was baffling. Which goods were wet? And why, since Papa had only one clothes rack, did the sign say "*Better* Dresses"? Shelf after shelf was laden with bolts of cloth, set slantwise so that prospective customers might study the thickness of the flannel or the gentle drape of a silk. I loved to watch Papa cut and measure. There was such authority in the way he thumped the bolt on the counter, such crispness in the snapping of the yardstick, such elegance in the way he held against the folded cloth a card of buttons or a frill of lace. "This makes up lovely. My wife, she made for our girls dresses you wouldn't believe, the very same broadcloth. Look, feel the quality. In the catalogue, thirty-nine cents a yard."

The catalogue was of course Eaton's. Papa took no notice of local competition, but he kept a sharp eye on what Eaton's was asking. I gathered that he was locked in a titanic struggle with Timothy Eaton for the custom of Birch Hills, Saskatchewan. Scholastic philosophers debating how many angels could dance on the point of a pin were not more rigorous than my father examining the various grades of Eaton's fleece-lined underwear. On the women's side of the store, his manner in these discussions was somewhat formal, reserved, abstract, as fitted a man dealing with female secrets. "You have here, nickel for nickel, a better drawer than Eaton's," he would say, lifting from its tissue wrapping a pair of winter bloomers. But, mindful of his customer's sensibilities, he neither fingered the good goods nor exposed the bloomer's mysterious inner construction. On the men's side, his manner changed dramatically. Here, in the smell of new leather and denim, he was bluff, hearty, hail-fellow-well-met. "See this gusset, this double crotch? You pitch hay all day, Nels, you don't split a seam. I stand back of it one hundred per cent. Two pair? Cash or charge?"

Mostly it was charge. In the last analysis, the O-Kay had just one big advantage over Eaton's: everything, even groceries, was to be had "on time." From harvest to harvest the farmer charged—sugar and flour and work gloves and overalls, patterns and percale, embroidery floss and rope and horses' feed bags, all moved across the counter. The figures in Papa's ledger mounted. He sent out bills regularly, but there was no question of payment before September. Everything depended upon the crops. And the crops, it seemed, depended upon a fearful number of contingencies. There was rain when we needed sun, or sun when we needed rain; the wheat might develop rust, or it might be beaten to the ground by one afternoon's hail. Some years grasshoppers, like biblical plagues, swept across the prairies harvesting the grain. So there it would be—September and no crop, or a crop of such low grade that the farmer had barely feed for his animals. No cash, more charge. Two years like this, and the O-Kay Store was bankrupt again.

Moving times were sad. There was first the unhealthy rush and confusion of the big final sale. "EVERYTHING MUST GO!" screamed the signs in the window. "GOODS SOLD BELOW COST!" At these times, Mama worked all day in the store, extra help bustled up and down the crowded aisles, and the cash register jingled.

"How come there is money?" I asked, tugging at the sagging edge of Papa's gray work sweater. "You said nobody had money."

Papa sighed. "Money to pay bills, no. But a little they have. A sale like this, a farmer has to take advantage."

Worst of all was the auction, when the contents of our house were spilled onto the lawn to be inspected, minutely described, and sold to the highest bidder. Even after two or three movings, I was never braced for the shocking melancholy of our possessions when they were exposed to public view. Most of the time I thought of our family as living, by rural standards, with a certain style, even grandeur. We always had a piano, a china cupboard full of wedding present silver, a proper dining room table with chairs that matched. Only on auction day, in the harsh September sunshine—or worse, in September rain, the furniture in tarpaulins and the buyers huddled under umbrellas —did I realize how thin was the veil of illusion. My mother's ferns, her cut-glass bowls and waxed bouquets of sweet peas, her crisp curtains and lace-edged cloths, had somehow blinded me to the truth, that our furniture was insubstantial as our hopes.

We left Birch Hills for Winnipeg the day of the first snow. I remember that I wandered out the back door, weary with waiting and restless in the silent house. On the last step I stood quite still a minute, mittened hands thrust into the pockets of my Hudson's Bay coat, my unbuckled galoshes flaring. All the way down to the ice house the yard was blue-white, sparkling. I thought of the times we had played fox and geese there, racing in wild circles as we cut the snow pie across and across and across, then scattering to the outer rim while the fox, dead center, decided who to chase. Today there was nobody to play with. I could throw myself down and make one last widewinged angel, but that would mean snow down my neck and snow powdering my good traveling clothes. We were leaving Saskatchewan, leaving the prairies forever. I lifted my foot and, heel to toe, heel to toe, stamped out my name in the snow. Freidele Bruser. Me. The letters, hard-packed, would ice over and disappear under wind-whipped drifts of white. In spring they would melt into the earth, or be borne as vapor through the skies. Other children would hunt for flowers in the April woods, swooping ecstatically on the first crocus or a round-eyed anemone with buds like bubbles of creamy satin. And none of them would know my name.

Why did I feel like crying? I *wanted* to go. Ever since I could remember, Winnipeg had been the golden city. Winnipeg was streetcars and cement sidewalks and stores —big stores, like Eaton's, floor after floor of unbelievable bliss. Winnipeg was libraries where you could take out five books at once and never pay anything as long as you returned them on time. Most of all, Winnipeg was belonging. In Birch Hills we were rootless. Winnipeg swept us up into a warm, laughing, weeping, extravagantly gesturing world of relations, all of whom rejoiced in the *naches* we brought them. ("A hundred in spelling!" my grandmother would say, wiping the tears from her eyes. "Oh, what a little head is this!") Whenever, in those days, I heard vaudeville performers tapping out the brisk melodies of "Golden Slippers" —"Oh, dem golden slippers To walk dem golden streets!" —I thought of Winnipeg. There, at last, my talents would be recognized. Writer? Singer? Musician? I wasn't sure. Anyway, I would *be* somebody. It was even possible that I might be discovered by a talent scout and carried off to Hollywood where, with my gift for elocution and my long black curls, I would replace the simpering heroine of the *Our Gang* comedies.

The train was fun at first. We opened the lunch basket right away, though it wasn't nearly suppertime, gorging ourselves on rich golden-tasting egg sandwiches and cold chicken washed down with gulps of thermos milk. I raced up and down the aisles testing my balance. I explored the wonders of the little bathroom—a real flush—peering into the steel toilet bowl and speculating about the ultimate destination of its contents. The trap opened; the track flashed past. No wonder the sign said, "Passengers will please refrain From using toilets on the train While the train is standing in the sta-tion." Just like a song, that sign. I hummed it softly to myself as I skipped back to our seat, hoping Mama wouldn't notice that my dress pocket was bulky where I'd hidden the bars of free soap. After a while I got tired of running for cups of ice water, so cold it made my teeth ache. "Where are the little bedrooms?" I asked. "Can I have an upper berth?"

Papa looked gray. "I'll get for you a pillow," Mama said quickly. "See, and your coat over your feet, like so?" There was to be no climbing the ladder, then, no porters drawing the thick curtain and saying, "Breakfast at eight, miss," the way they did in books. I supposed it was because of the Depression. I hadn't the faintest idea what the Depression was—something about wheat and stocks and money— but I knew it was a bad thing. Still, we were moving to Winnipeg because of the Depression; sometimes a bad thing made a good thing. . . . And there was a song about "Prosperity is just around the corner"—or was it "Happy days are here again?" I pulled my coat up under my chin, breathing in the nice sweetish-damp smell of the wolf collar, and slept.

The CPR station was noisier than I remembered, and more confusing. There seemed to be miles of track, criss-crossing like the lines on a snakes and ladders board, with freight cars shunting back and forth. In the yellow-brown

light of the domed terminal, we huddled beside our bags.
Groups of animated strangers embraced joyfully or clung
to each other outside the heavy gates. Negro porters—
Papa called them darkies—rushed past. In their stiff blue
uniforms and round caps, they looked surprisingly like the
blackface comedians who had provided, until now, my
chief images of the African world. Nobody said, "Hello,
Freidele." I stamped my feet, numb in the drafty station,
and blew on my mittens. "Soon," Mama said. "They come
very soon. It's hard for Mendel. With his rheumatism he
don't move fast."

Until Papa got settled in a new store, we were to stay
with Fayge and Mendel. I understood the reasons for this
bleak arrangement: Baba and Zayde, my grandparents,
were not strong; Aunt Lucy was a bride with a tiny
apartment. Fayge and Mendel, on the other hand, had
plenty of room and no children. They occupied the most
spotless house I had ever known. There every gleaming
table featured a starched doily, every doily a cut-glass bowl
or vase in which dried everlasting flowers curled brittle
petals against Time. Kitchen and bathroom alike gave off
harsh institutional odors, the smell of severity and soap.
Mendel ignored us, Fayge undertook to set our lives in
order. "*I told you so many times. . . .*" The familiar phrase
formed on her lips as she hurried towards us. She had
told us my father would never make a living in the country.
She had told us a Jew belonged with his own people. She
had told us the children would grow up like wild ones,
with hardly a word of Yiddish. As we jounced along on
the streetcar, clutching our suitcases and shopping bags,
our throats thick with train dust, she poured over us an
avalanche of good advice. For supper there was *helzel,*

chicken skin stuffed with greasy crumbs, and a peculiarly dreadful jelly made from chicken feet soaked in brine. I rose from the table, stomach heaving, flung myself on my bed—and slid. Cousin Fayge had given me a rubber sheet.

Winnipeg in 1931 was not the golden city. It was, in effect, several homogeneous cities grouped around the main arteries of Portage Avenue and Main Street. Portage was brisk, busy, modern, a wide avenue with central boulevards down which the streetcars clanged. Its heart was Eaton's, an imposing building of that dark-red brick which has ever since seemed to me the color of commerce. Across from Eaton's glittered the Metropolitan and the Capitol, posh movie theaters whose flashing signs, in that pre-neon era, stirred me like the vision of a diamond chain shaken against black velvet skies. Several blocks west, on a wind-whipped corner, stood the Hudson's Bay Store, aristocratically white and serene, with an atmosphere glacial as its name. The Bay marked an end to the business district. Above it, in one direction, Portage dropped away to a trail of shabby booksellers and used car dealers; in the other, swinging around the open Mall, lay the new auditorium where stuffed buffalo guarded exhibits of Indian artifacts and, every spring, fiddles and young voices sang out in the annual music festival. Still further along the Mall and south of Portage stood the nobly proportioned Parliament Buildings, one of the city's few grandeurs, with a statue of the Golden Boy poised above its great dome and lawns sweeping down to the university buildings on one side, the Assiniboine River on the other. Winnipeg, our history texts assured us, was the gateway to the West; the Osborne Bridge over the Assiniboine constituted the gateway to Winnipeg's exclusive South End and the mansions of Wellington Crescent.

The South End was white Anglo-Saxon Protestant; the North End was swarthy, European, Hebrew or Greek and Russian Orthodox. To reach the North End you traveled along Main Street (main only in the days of old Winnipeg) past an untidy clutter of Jewish pawnbroking establishments, Ukrainian bookstores, Polish communal associations, and Russian herbariums. Here were the cheap movie houses (ten cents for a double feature, free dishes on dish night), the wholesalers, the seedy furniture stores featuring waterfall bedroom sets and multilingual signs. (*We speak German, Yiddish, Polish* . . . whatever *you* speak.) In every doorway, in those days, lounged gypsy women with dirty head kerchiefs and brilliant black eyes. "Your fortune, lady? Read your palm?" They came like locusts or dust storms, like an act of God. One year they smoldered all up and down Main Street, the next year they vanished and I never saw a gypsy again. The boundary of the business district here was the Royal Alexandra Hotel, a poor relation of the Fort Garry to the south. (The relationship between the two hotels was roughly that of Eaton's to the Bay, North End to South, immigrant to Old Settler.) Beyond the Royal Alex, appropriately under a gloomy railroad bridge, Main Street deteriorated steadily past the slums of Higgins and Jarvis to a land of corned beef and rye bread, the lively steaming ghetto of Winnipeg's Jews.

There were other inner cities too in 1931: a new France in St. Boniface, built around hospital and cathedral; Elmwood; remote Kildonan; Fort Rouge, Riel's old territory. But of course I had always assumed we would live in the North End, with *unzere,* our people. What a shock, then, to find that Papa's new store was in alien territory, south but not stylish south. Sherbrooke was an urban prairie, street after dismal street of low, rackety wooden houses, not a theater or a department store in sight. The names over the doorbells were Scottish and Scandinavian; we would once again be singular in our Jewishness. As for our new city business—it didn't seem like a real store at all. Papa had bought—how diminishing—a neighborhood candy store.

Actually, the Sherburne Confectionery wasn't just candy. We sold odds and ends of groceries too. There was a refrigerator for milk and slippery-looking luncheon meat (mostly gristle and gelatin, with olive slices for decoration), a revolving rack of novelty toys, a magazine stand. It was a sort of depot, a place where housewives ran in, wearing bedroom slippers, for the tin of peas they'd forgotten to buy at the Piggly Wiggly. We stayed open evenings—that was the loaf-of-bread-for-sandwiches trade—and Sunday mornings, so customers could pick up the paper. From eight in the morning till ten at night Mama and Papa were on call. When business was quiet, they sat in the front room—only a curtain separated it from the store—listening for the bell. I got used to being interrupted in the midst of a sentence (*"Heisst!* Someone comes!"*) or to seeing Papa's glass of tea with *verenye* grown cold where he had left it. Store and house together stood smack on a corner. There was no yard, and sidewalks ran directly by our windows. All day long passers-by looked into the kitchen and dining room. Not, I think, with any special curiosity; we were just *there*. Even the bedrooms, up a narrow flight of stairs, felt public. Standing at the windows in my cambric nightie, I could see in the distance the flickering electric signs of Sargent Street. One, advertising chocolate bars, had a kind of dreadful fascination. "FAT EMMA"—a circus lady outlined in red—flashed, pranced, and vanished; "PIE FACE," a Chaplinesque figure, emaciated blue. And then "EAT-EAT-EAT." Even with the blinds drawn, my room flashed red and blue until, staring at the ceiling, I fell asleep.

In the store, Papa worked hard to build up business. It was heavy going because the Ferrantis, who preceded us, watered the milk and gave short weight. Gradually suspicion faded—no one, seeing Papa in action, could have supposed him adept in trickery—but only to be replaced by a faintly amused condescension. Papa, so wonderful with farmers, was wrong for the city neighborhood trade. Finishing one of his Russian stories—"So the marriage broker says, 'Well, she is maybe just a *little* bit hunchbacked!'" —he would look up radiant, expecting applause. The housewife, juggling her grocery bag, would smile in a strained way and make an ambiguous noise, something between "Hmm" and "Haa." Or, even worse, would break in at the climactic moment, the big scene, with, "Excuse me, Bruser, but the old man's waiting for the bologna." When that happened, Papa finished telling the story anyway, to Mama or to me. We feigned joy.

The disappointment of the new store was nothing compared to the horror of the new school. I tried to tell myself, that first morning, what fun it would be. Different teachers, a whole crowd of new friends. But really I knew better. Sometimes in Birch Hills there would be a new girl. I remembered how we whispered together at recess, Fern and Hazel and I, and how, if she came up with her ball or rope, we linked arms and skipped away, screaming in private mirth. Still, I tried to be happy. I had a new dress, made specially for my debut—a soft plum-colored wool, with matching panties banded at the knee. My coat was too short (a pity) but Mama had knitted me a white angora bonnet with great crisp chocolate-box bows, rosettes of gorgeous pink taffeta bursting over each ear. I had white stockings (most girls wore black or dreary brown) drawn on so carefully, the fleece underwear folded at the ankle and held tight, that you could hardly see the bumps underneath. Mama and Papa walked me to the corner. "Don't forget you give to the teacher your report card, and the letter from the Birch Hills principal!" Mama said. Papa pressed my hand. "You walk into the room, is not necessary a report card. *They* know the bright eyes."

I had seen Gladstone School once before, from the streetcar, but close up it looked larger. In Birch Hills, the school was hardly bigger than our house. It stood in grass and trees, surrounded by the cluster of outdoor toilets and a row of hitching posts where, all day long, horses with comical nose bags munched their oats and waited for their riders to burst out at the four o'clock bell. Gladstone was gray stone set in a frozen pool of asphalt, and there was a steel mesh fence, of a type I had seen once before around a menacing construction marked "Danger. High Voltage. Keep Out." A huge metal cylinder, maybe ten feet in diameter, sprouted from the ground beside the school. Big as a silo, it rose all the way to the top floor, where it thrust out an arm to the adjoining window.

"What *is* this?" I asked a girl who leaned against the mysterious pipe.

"You mean the fire escape?"

"*Fire escape?*" In Birch Hills we had a special ladder. . . . "How do you work it?"

"Oh, it's keen. When the alarm goes, you run for that door, see? Then you slither into the tube and *whoosh*, all the way down!" Her hand described a terrifying vertical.

So this was school in the city. Fire drills, maybe even fires. Hundreds of children rushing for that narrow escape door, and me such a poor runner, last in every race. The metal would heat up. What would it feel like, hurtling down that glowing, fiercely throbbing pipe? Would the door at the base open, flinging us out onto the asphalt? Or would we all collect in a heap at the bottom, curling up like maple leaves in an autumn bonfire?

"Hey, Porky, you new?" A boy in Lindberg aviator helmet and goggles poked my arm.

I nodded.

"What nationality are you?"

That was a crazy question. "I'm Canadian. From Saskatchewan."

"Not that, stupid. I mean, like are you Italian?" His eyes added up details. Swarthy complexion, black hair too tightly curled. . . . "French?"

Always before I had been known as Jewish; I'd never been obliged to identify myself publicly. Other children were crowding around. I considered saying, "Russian." That would be true enough, my parents came from the Ukraine. And it wasn't as if we were religious, or went to synagogue. . . . . "I'm Jewish," I said.

This announcement produced a stunning effect. Leather helmet placed his hands on his hips, cocked his head to one side and surveyed me with an expression of incredulous delight. "Well, how about that? It's a Jew. A real little, live little, fat little kike! Sing us a song, Jew. *Jakey, Isaac, Ab-ra-ham. We're the boys that don't eat ham!*"

I clutched my schoolbag and tried to edge towards the school door. Hopeless. They were all in it now. Galoshes, mackinaws, caps, helmets, toques. . . . I wished I hadn't worn the angora bonnet.

"Ask her if her old man has a chopped-off dink!" somebody called. "Isn't that what they do to Jew boys, trim their little piddlers?"

"Ask her if she's got any matzo sandwiches in her bag! Say, Porky, is it true they make those matzos out of Christian blood?"

Someone tore at my bonnet. The ribbon gave with a silky, swishing sound.

"Give me back my hat!"

"She wants her hat! Here fellas, give her back her cute little hat!"

The bonnet sailed over the heads of the crowd.

"Take it to the road!" A girl's voice. "Take it to the road and fill it with horse paddies!"

A group detached itself from the throng and dashed off on this new errand. Leather helmet leaned forward, his voice now an exaggerated stage whisper. "Say, Porky—" A broad grin, hideously intimate. "Can I have a f-f-f-f-f-f . . . ?"

The appalling consonant—thick, fleshy, suggestive—sputtered outrageously. I could almost smell the hot strong ammonia odor of the school toilets, see the unspeakable obscenities scrawled on the dirty walls. "Let me by!"

The boy moved back a step, cherry-pit eyes shining. "Can I have a f-f-f-f-f-f-*few matches?*"

Hoots of delight. What a wit!

I had never been good at name-calling. The worst insult I knew—"You're a turkey-spotted, chicken-livered fool!"—was clearly inadequate. But I knew what a teacher would say, or a parent. "You ought to wash your mouth out with soap!"

"Why, shame on you, Porky!" The boy shook his head, astonished now at my depraved imagination. "You thought I was going to ask you for a fu-fu-fu-fu-fu-fu-FULL BOX!"

I learned at Gladstone School the many faces of defeat. It waited for me daily in the playground and on the stairs. Above all—this I could never, never have anticipated—it waited in the classroom. In Birch Hills I had been star scholar, first in class. My reading, my spelling, my compositions were admired and exclaimed over. Special jobs, like carrying notes to the principal or cleaning the blackboard, fell to me naturally. And from this great eminence, I tumbled into the dunce's corner. "Have you done fractions?" the new teacher prodded. "No? What about the area of a circle?" Terror froze my tongue. Arithmetic had never been my strong point. At Gladstone we had daily speed drills, with the numbers on a big cardboard clock. "Five and 7—5 and 11—5 and 22—5 and 13 . . ." The pointer moved. I counted desperately on my fingers, never fast enough. The day Miss Brinton discovered I didn't know my times tables (in Birch Hills we used exercise books with tables printed on the back), she told me to gather up my books. I was transferred to Lower Four.

Here Mrs. Murphy—fat, lumpy, streamy-haired—addressed me with weary patience, articulating each word as if I were a case of severe brain damage. Lessons proceeded with the agonizing deliberateness of a slow-motion film, but it was through an unfamiliar landscape that I floated. In Saskatchewan, grade four history had been Canadian explorers; in Manitoba it was British kings. Geography plunged me, unprepared, into darkest Africa—and into the most dreadful of my humiliations.

I had been waiting, forever it seemed, for some chance to redeem myself. Surely the moment must come when my teacher perceived that I was not really stupid. But weeks passed. Easter report cards would soon be issued. What would Mama and Papa say when they knew I was failing arithmetic, hanging by a hair in everything else? I imagined the scene in our kitchen: Mama weeping softly into a dish towel; Papa brave, confronting the wreck of his dreams. . . . Mrs. Murphy stood at the front of the room, the geography book braced against her formidable bosom. "Now we *con-tin-ue,* class, we *go on* with our African journey. Keep your finger on the place, please. 'Heavy rainstorms are peculiar to this region. . . .'" She looked up, nailing us to our seats with a new word. *"Pee-kyul-yar.* Now, what does that mean?"

"Funny," someone said. "Queer."

Mrs. Murphy nodded. "Very good. Heavy rainstorms would be funny here, strange. In other words, no heavy rainstorms. Right, class?"

I raised my hand. Geography might be mystery unfathomable, but language I knew. Galileo before the Inquisition could hardly have spoken with more reckless assurance. "Oh, no, Mrs. Murphy. It's the other way around. 'Peculiar' means *strange* sometimes. Only here it means *characteristic of."*

If I hadn't been so nearsighted, I might have seen Mrs. Murphy's florid countenance turn tyrian purple. But I saw nothing except the chance, at last, to show who I was. "So you see," I continued happily, "this must be a country that has *lots* of rain."

In the dreadful silence that followed, Mrs. Murphy streaked down the aisle. (Who would have thought such bulk could move so swiftly?) Then, pulling my arm, she thumped me towards the front of the room and opened her desk drawer. "Hold out your hand!"

I had seen children strapped, often. But that sort of treatment was for incorrigibles. At home, I had never experienced any punishment more severe than a gravely disappointed look. And now here I stood, before a roomful of strangers, one of them holding a thick rubber belt. Timidly I extended my palm. I did mean to keep it there, but the sight of the strap descending was too much. I withdrew my hand sharply and put it behind my back. The belt struck Mrs. Murphy's thigh with a dreadful thwack. She screamed, the class exploded with delight, and then she caught my hand and, gripping my wrist, brought the strap down again and again. "I'll teach you to talk back to me, you little smart aleck, you! You're not in Palestine now, you know!" That astonished me. No one in my family had ever been to Palestine. "We don't need your kind to tell us what's what!"

Back at my desk, I put my head in my arms and sobbed. What *was* my kind? The old boundaries had dissolved. To be punished for not knowing would have seemed harsh, but just. To be punished for knowing was a negation of life. I felt like the little old lady in a Mother Goose rhyme that always scared me. She fell asleep, and while she slept a thief cut off her skirt above the knees. After that she roamed unrecognized, unrecognizable even to her little dog. "Oh dearie me, dearie me, can this be I?"

I ran almost all the way home. Now, in April, March snows had turned to muddy slush. Children dashed by on bicycles, racing to games I had never played—jacks, alleys, tippy-cat, kick the can. In Birch Hills, everyone would be making paper boats, fashioning them secretly in school out of shiny foolscap and sailing them down the streams that flowed under wooden sidewalks. "I will tell Papa and Mama," I thought. "And they will tell the principal and he will talk to Mrs. Murphy. . . ." And then what? Live out the year under a furious teacher's eye? Afflict my parents with the burden of my misery? I slowed up and wiped my nose on my sleeve. By the time I banged open the kitchen door I was even humming (not too richly) the chorus from "Flow Gently, Sweet Afton."

In the kitchen an apple pie steamed under a rough linen towel. Mama stood at the sink, her arms plunged to the elbows in suds. "There is a tart for you!" she called. She pushed her hair back from her forehead, leaving a froth of rainbow-colored bubbles glimmering along one dark strand. "Eat maybe outside, the kitchen is hot from the oven." I snatched up the tart and my red rubber ball and ran, grateful to escape the usual loving review. ("You got your homework all right, yes? The teacher read your composition?")

Onesie-twosies was a game I could play by myself. I bounced the ball halfheartedly against the side of our store. "Plainie-plainies, clappie-clappies. . . ." I was up to twistie-wristies when Papa came out and stood a minute, watching.

"An Eskimo pie, sweetheart?"

I shook my head.

"Maybe you want to work the adding machine?" That was a rare treat. Usually I loved to sit on the big stool punching out numbers while Papa read aloud from his ledger.

"No thank you." *Pung. Pung.* Ball slammed against brick.

It was funny about Papa. You could fool him—easy—on little things. On big things you couldn't fool him at all. "What's the matter?" he asked. "You don't feel good?"

"I feel fine!" I missed on spin-aroundies. The ball rolled down the sidewalk and plopped into a muddy puddle.

Papa bent down, picked up the ball and wiped it on his store apron till it shone like a fresh-picked apple. Then he put it in my hand. "A Jew is a wanderer," he said, "and he learns, so, to carry with him what matters. It is not easy, a new school, new people. But what you are, in the heart and the head, no one takes from you. Do not worry, my child. *He that gave us teeth will give us bread.*"

I put the ball in my pocket and ran down the street. My feet felt oddly light without rubbers, and the breeze blew my hair. Garfield Street, Ingersoll, Goulding, Anderson. . . . I'd never been this far before. The stucco houses were farther apart now; there were vacant lots that looked fun to explore. A sign said Greenwood Street. That was nice, after all the names of statesmen. And this—almost a real meadow. There was a grove of poplars, the tips of bare branches already faintly pink and swelling with buds. It would be a good place to bring sandwiches in a month or so. Perhaps there would be strawberries here in summer. And the soil looked right for purple crocus. . . . I knelt on the damp earth, poking the matted grass to look for new shoots.

THE O-KAY STORE

NEVILLE, Foam Lake, Humboldt, Birch Hills. Winnipeg. (I attended school and college there, a thirteen-year span, but for my father it was a brief, disastrous interlude that persuaded him he could never make a living in the city.) Altona, Gretna, Plum Coulee. . . . The towns rolled by. Pages torn from a calendar, windblown seeds from a dandelion, they marked the rise and fall of stores. But always, above and beyond individual ventures there shone, like the perpetual star, multifoliate rose, the eternal idea of The O-Kay Store. And that is what I remember most strongly from all those years of defeat—my father's joyous conviction that *next* time we would prevail. It was an attitude—an instinct, really—that shaped his entire life.

Papa was born in Gravskoya, one of those poverty-stricken Russian villages where Jews scratched a thin living from the soil. His father, my Zayde, was a wine merchant with small knowledge of wine and no talent for selling. (He must, I think, have been very like Papa. Certainly he bequeathed to Boris, the second son, his own unerring instinct for failure.) White bread was a rare treat in that household. Sometimes, on very special holidays, a herring was baked in the middle of the loaf and each child got a slice. "You can't imagine how *geshmack* it was, that bread," Papa used to tell us. "Such a taste of herring."

Both my parents grew up in Czarist Russia, but their tales of the Old World were strikingly different. Mama had stories about pogroms. Papa seemed never to have been looking out the window when Cossacks rode by. "Tell me when you were little," I begged. "Tell about the soldiers."

"So what should I tell?" Papa shrugged. "I was a boy, a *cheder* student. I read Torah. I dreamed."

"Didn't you do *anything* else?"

"Sometimes I looked after the cow, the chickens."

This was a new fact. Having watched Papa wrestle with the simplest practical tasks, I tried to imagine him tending livestock. "Did you feed them?" I asked.

He laughed. "This no. But I thought always how nice it was, the life of the rooster."

I remember another poultry story from this period. For weeks before Passover, Grandmother had been fattening a goose. Daily Papa watched her force grain down the creature's throat, and daily his imagination fed on dreams of the feast to come. Roast goose in a tender bed of potatoes . . . golden soup with rich dumplings . . . crisp onion curls fried in goose fat. . . . At last he could stand it no longer. Taking advantage of a moment when his mother was busy in the kitchen, he snatched the goose from its pen and ran with it to the *shochet*, the ritual slaughterer. At the door he was met by a hard-faced maid. "Too late. The master is at supper."

"Is necessary."

Bird in hand, he pushed past the startled girl and into the dining room, where the good man sat already at table. Candles flickered on the damask cloth, the family faces shone with the first intimations of *gefilte* fish. "*Idiot!*"

roared the shoychet. "What is it you do here, right to the table with a goose?"

Papa was terrified. "Mama said—we want you should kill it."

The shoychet flung down his spoon. *"God in heaven, what a head!* So how come you don't put it right in the soup?"

At this point in the story, Papa always lowered his eyes in an attitude of holy meekness. "I thought it was a funny thing, yes. But when a learned man asks—what else could I do?"

Papa was eighteen when he set out for Odessa to become a great painter. That such a family—simple, pious, poor— should have countenanced his ambition seems strange. I suppose they had decided the boy was good for nothing else. In Odessa Papa grew his hair, adopted the flowing ties and tight suits of the dandy, learned photography, and waited for fame. It was a long time coming. He got tired. ("What did you find in Odessa, Papa?" I asked one day. "I found—I found that to be hungry in Gravskoya and hungry in Odessa is the same thing.") With hope in his heart and all his worldly possessions in two canvas bags, he set sail for America.

New York in 1906 was, to a lad from the Ukraine, unbelievable splendor. The big buildings, the fine well-fed faces, the prosperous rush and bustle, everybody in good goods. . . . In the middle of Grand Central Station, Papa set down his bags. *This* was living, yes. He would open a studio, just a little one to begin with. People would come from all over. ("You know somebody wants a photograph, you take him to Bruser. A picture he makes, you can't tell it from life.") The *Mama* and *Tata* he would bring from

Gravskoya, they should have comfort in their old age. And for himself, then, a marriage, such a wife, a real sparkler —black snapping eyes, bosoms like ripe apples. . . . And the children . . . His heart flowed over at the thought of them, the boy a scholar with the head of an old man, the little girls healthy and beautiful just like the *Mama*. . . . He must get started at once. He reached for his bags. They were gone.

After the Grand Central disaster Papa had hard going. He learned to live from the beer parlors. Not drinking, you understand—"God forbid a Jew should be a drunkard"—but from pretzels supplied free by the management. He picked up a little money doing street portraits. He began to dream again. (He did not buy the Brooklyn Bridge, but that was because no one offered it to him. Not until much later did he begin purchasing gold mines. He was the only man I ever knew who *actually* bought a gold brick. I believe it came in a paper bag.) Next stop: Canada, a new world newer even than America.

Papa departed for Vancouver, but his money ran out at Winnipeg. Well, if God chose Winnipeg, who was he to argue? Within a year he had made enough as a photographer to send for his parents, and a new scheme flowered. Why should his father not act as a kind of salesman for the business? A dignified old Jew in black broadcloth, a beard like silk, who could refuse him? Orders would pour in . . . money . . . a fine marriage, such a wife. . . . But he had reckoned without Grandpa. Willing he was. Boris said, "Go, *Tata*," and he went. But he knew what was really important, and he was not a man to let mere practical considerations interfere with ultimate goods. He knocked on the door, he showed the samples. "These pictures my son makes, hand color. Reasonable." The housewife reached for her purse. And then Grandpa would sigh, the sigh of God's servant. "*Oy, vay*, my daughter. For what do you need such a thing? A picture, a piece paper with a face? Books a man must have, and bread. But pictures? Who needs pictures?"

The business did not prosper. Papa, reduced once more to bread without herring, succumbed to the call of the wild. He opened a general store in Neville, Saskatchewan. Some men, now, looking out on the immense bleakness of the prairies, the flat sky and flatter land, would have said to themselves, "Well, this is it. The grand adventure is over. I am stuck here." Not Papa. What looked like a dead horse, or a wooden one, might prove a going concern. Surely the Almighty, who had brought his people out of Egypt and rained down manna in the wilderness, would not let him starve in Saskatchewan? (There must have been some days when his faith wavered. An entry in his 1912 ledger for Wednesday, the day when the weekly train brought farmers to town, reads: "Wednesday. Mail Day. Ten cents." Meantime, in Winnipeg, his parents had found him a bride. Papa hurried back to meet Yetta, his heart on fire. A surprise. Yetta was a blessing in disguise—and such a disguise! Rotten teeth, a face like a pancake. . . . Still, one doesn't know a package from its wrappings. The engagement was announced. To cheer himself, Papa went one evening to a lecture at the Talmud Torah. Afterwards, he could never remember what that lecture was about—only that he saw a girl, and fell in love.

"Was she very beautiful?" I used to ask when he told me the familiar tale.

"Beautiful, yes. But not just the face. Pretty faces I had seen before. This was from within."

My mother was a young girl then, seventeen to his twenty-five, besieged by suitors and amused at the hick who proposed marriage on first meeting. Papa broke his engagement, returned to the country, and proceeded to court his beloved by mail. As long as Jacob strove for Rachel he wrote her. The series of letters begins, "Dear Friend . . . I remain with respect and sincerity, B. Bruser," and ends, in an ecstasy of exclamation points, "Oh, you dear, sweet Ronachka!!! . . . . Yours, and only yours forever, Boris." When I was a child, I admired these communications chiefly for the little watercolor pictures with which they were embellished: a bouquet of flowers enclosing two hearts, a boy observing his sweetheart hugging a pet rabbit ("Oh, I wish I was a rabbit!"), and, finally, a man's hand holding a gold ring. Years later I discovered in them my father's true gift. He was indeed "an artist," as we always said—whose natural medium was language, not paint. His spoken English retained always that slight oddness of inflection and syntax which marks the foreign-born; his written English, on the other hand, flowed with an ease remarkable in one who learned the language late and spent few years in school. Here are all the qualities I recognize. He is frantic over a delayed letter. "Nothing on Saturday, the same dish on Tuesday. I was badly struck and didn't know what to think, and there are so many cars and jitneys (the last unknown to me yet), so many crossings that always endanger the traffic, and here my imagination went wild . . . pictures of horror before me. . . . Please, don't laugh at me, darling." Mention of skating produces a response only slightly less intense. "I must ask you again, not to skate at all now, unless the ice is thick and heavy." He worries that letters may go astray ("Please write in plain letters, NEVILLE, Sask., as

there is a town by the name MELVILLE") or that insuffi-
cient stamps may doom her precious envelope to the dead-
letter office. "You must know, those people are very strict,
almost cruel. The letter that means so much to me carries
no weight with them, they will bury it, it will be gone forever." Often there appears a touching moral earnestness, the
tone of an older man (he was past thirty when he married)
anxious to instruct without wearying a light-hearted girl. "I
am glad to hear you are having a good time, but not
attending every dance. There is nothing in it, dear. A dance
once in a while is all right, but not as a regular habit."
"Never mind if I am not handsome" (something specious
here, he well knew his dashing good looks). "You possess
beauty enough for us both. Besides, it is almost a rule of
nature, a good-looking girl gets a homely fellow and vice
versa. (Of course I don't think I am all that bad.) I am
healthy, sober and kind-hearted, have all the means to provide a comfortable living for you. I love you dearly, and a
little affection in return will satisfy me." Even in the first
rapture of acceptance, he writes to urge, "Tell your parents
all that has passed between us. They have reared you, and
it is their highest destiny in life to see you happy." One of
my favorite letters is characteristic in its combination of
conscious loftiness with subdued self-mockery. "Today is one
of our finest and most momentous holidays, *Shovuos*, the
day when the Ten Commandments, the foundation of real
civilization, were proclaimed to our forefathers. This holiday
recalls to me my childhood, those happy and innocent hours
when full of joy I tramped the green fields, gathering arm-
loads of blossoms in honor of *Shovuos*. In those glorious
days I was convinced that our village was the universe, its

Jewish inhabitants the only people—and blintzes the finest dish in the world."

My parents' wedding photograph is sepia brown. They are posed, the two of them, in the manner of such period pictures, against the curtained backdrop that opens on a painted scene. My mother stands, all drapery and gauze. Pearls cluster like grapes in her gathered veil; her hair swoops deeply beneath it, skeined silk. Richness and profusion flow in the bouquet with its streaming ferns, the train that falls from her headdress into a satin pool. Beside her, in a carved straight chair, my father is a model of stylish severity: Celluloid collar, snapped back at the throat in crisp points; dark cutaway jacket, pinstriped trousers, precisely buttoned spats and high-shine shoes. The rose in his lapel, the gold finger ring, provide elegant grace notes. For all her romantic costume, my mother appears singularly present, collected. I know that look. Ten years later, it will say, "Have you got a clean hankie?" Now it mirrors perhaps a practical awareness of packing to be done before the train leaves. She looks directly at the photographer. And my father—ah, my father! The eyes belie the look. He contemplates an infinitely distant scene, and I know that when the shutter clicking is over, he will have trouble finding the tickets.

My father went to the country to make a quick fortune and stayed almost fifty years. Logically, he should have been a success in business: he had intelligence, charm, style, a buoyant good humor. All these gifts, however, worked against him with marvelous consistency. His intelligence was abstract, better suited to the refinements of biblical commentary than to invoices from Midwest grocers. He composed eloquent ads and sales circulars—far over the heads of his rural audience. He won the affection of his customers, but not their loyalty; that ran along racial and religious lines. He could sell, but not collect payment. Above all, he could not learn mistrust. Under his indulgent eye errand boys grew rich, dashing off on deliveries whose proceeds never reached the till. ("Why does Eric put money in his apron pocket, Papa?" "He has sore feet, that way he doesn't run all the time to the register.") Penniless clerks, after a few years in my father's employ, opened up fine new establishments across the street. ("It's natural the farmers go now to Arnason. He is from their church.")

He took his greatest trouncing, however, from "one of our own." This dreadful event occurred during the midthirties. Papa's Winnipeg confectionery had failed, but we continued to live in the city so that my sister and I might reap the benefits of good schools and a Jewish community life. My father was between stores. Regularly he made trips to outlying villages, returning with a melancholy shrug. "You could bury yourself there." The times alarmed. Shabby men thronged the wood yard where relief tickets were handed out; our menu featured fish-cutting stew more often than, strictly speaking, we cared to have it. One evening my father came back exultant. "Rona! I have today bought a business!"

My mother was making *kreplach*. She placed a dab of cheese on the dough and pinched it in carefully. "You mean you've *decided* already."

"Decided, signed, is ours. A real store. Last year twenty-five thousand dollars they grossed."

The *kreplach* dropped into the boiling pot with a sharp plopping noise. I could always tell when my mother was controlling herself; her movements became slower, deliberate. "Boris, in one day you don't take inventory. How can you buy when you don't know *what?*"

He laughed, hugging her, delighted with his acumen, his unusual efficiency. "Rona, Goldstein is a Jew, from the Ukraine, a Mason. When a Mason gives his word, you don't need inventory."

My mother left with him next day to survey our good fortune. They returned very quiet, Papa gentler even than usual and oddly apologetic. As I ran to the Piggly Wiggly for vegetables, Mama reminded me, "Old carrots, not new," and I understood that we were not, after all, about to enter the Promised Land. I never saw Goldstein's store. Its acquisition, though, marked a new period in our lives. Mama would be home for a few days, baking and cooking, filling the icebox; then she was off on the bus to help with the clearance sale. The entire stock had to be sold, the store was not worth continuing—that was all I knew. Only years later did I hear, from my mother, the whole story. My father had been taken, completely. She saw that at first glance. Half-empty cartons, water-damaged goods, flour polluted by mice, stale tobaccos, faded cotton, and frayed silks . . . a dead pig in a poke. "Couldn't you have done something?" I asked. My mother sighed. "I could have stopped the check, yes. But what would that do to him? Boris Bruser, a businessman, and his wife has to mix in? No, I knew we could dig out. With pride." She began to laugh. "*Oy,* but there was a minute, when I showed Papa what his Mason sold us. He was ready to tear himself to pieces. And then, what do you think he said, your papa the criminal, the man who can't rest if he has a nickel doesn't belong to him? 'I will burn it,' he said, 'for insurance.'"

Papa dug out of that disaster and into others. He began to think in terms of alternative schemes. He would equip a caravan and send it over the country roads, selling merchandise from house to house. ("You'll give to *Steve* this job?" Mama said. "A *frage*. He carries away goods all the time under his jacket. A caravan he don't need.") He would breed chinchillas, raise sheep. He would open a post on Hudson's Bay. He would convert to self-serve, the coming thing. One day he announced a scheme for attracting more customers on Saturday night: an ice cream parlor, staffed by pretty girls who would ply susceptible males with vanilla fudge and then funnel them discreetly into dry goods, where they might fall easy prey to underwear. (This scheme had only two disadvantages: the shortage of pretty girls, and the total absence of refrigeration.) Meanwhile, in the store of the moment, farmers outfitted by Eaton's bought sugar "on time." The handwriting was not just on the wall; it was in the ledger (Accounts Overdue) and in the stack of unpaid invoices threatening bankruptcy.

How, in the face of all this, could Papa continue cheerful? "He must have money put away," my sister said. I think I glimpsed the true explanation the day I cracked the code. Like all storekeepers, Papa had a secret system for recording, on price tickets, the actual cost of merchandise. A tag might read, "$2.98." And underneath, RNE. I used to badger him for the code; he always put me off. Gradually the idea grew that I might crack the system myself. "X," often repeated, almost certainly meant a double digit. "R" was one, and "F," nine. Papa had told me work gloves cost twenty-four dollars a dozen, so OEX must be $2.00. One by one clues accumulated. When I finally discovered that "M" equaled five, I felt like an alchemist who has found the philosopher's stone. "R=1; O=2; N=3; A=4. . . ." Of course. There it was, from one to ten, my father's secret. RONA MY LIFE.

Papa's last store was in Grandview, a Manitoba town that looked very much like all the other towns we had tried. "This time," Papa said, "we make a go of it. You'll see." I looked bleakly about me, unconvinced. Older now—at the last auction, we had sold my toys along with the household goods—I viewed the new enterprise with an adolescent's knowing skepticism. The building—store and dwelling combined, an arrangement I had come to dread—was, if anything, more depressing than the last, a great box sheathed in corrugated metal that clattered hideously in bad weather. The house smelled of sour milk, the store of sweat and cheese. In the kitchen, Mama was ripping up old linoleum, moaning softly at the unspeakable discoveries between each layer. I stayed in the store, conducting my own fascinatingly dreadful explorations. The fabric on the bolts was faded, the puffed wheat chocolate bars had worms. The shallow glass display boxes fronting the grocery counter contained substances so ancient, so close to total disintegration, that barley was scarcely to be distinguished from coffee beans. Papa sat on the high stool at his desk, composing.

"'Grand opening of The O-Kay Store,'" he declaimed. "'It's our birthday, but you get the presents.' Sounds good, eh?"

I feigned enthusiasm. "Mmm. Terrific."

"I make it, you see, like a letter to the farmers, signed B. Bruser, manager a whole chain of stores in western Canada."

"Papa!" I was shocked. "How can you say a thing like that? They'll find out we've got just this one store."

"So? In Gretna haven't I been? In Altona, all the other places? This doesn't make a chain?"

Grandview seemed something less than a bustling metropolis, but then, as the Goodyear traveler pointed out, it was a Saturday night town. Over the sample cases and the wholesale catalogues of rubber footwear, he filled us in. "You buy right and sell right, Bruser, you got yourself a nice living here. Dead all week—bread, bologna, package of matches. But wait'll you see them wagons come Saturday night. Place really jumps."

Papa brightened. "You think maybe I have Saturday specials? Big signs in the window, an ad in the paper maybe?"

The salesman shook his head. "Nah. That stuff don't go around here. These Polacks pick themselves a store like it's a club, see, and that's it. You get the big boys—Steve Worchuk, say, or Pete Wyrzynowski—and you got it made. They'll bring their whole damn church."

The big boys, I thought, must be venerable community patriarchs. It was a real surprise when the first of them appeared. I was opening a shipment of penny candy, checking the boxes against the invoice—2 cinnamon hearts, 1 mint leaves—when a voice demanded, "Them fresh?" I looked. The newcomer scooped up a handful of jawbreakers, grinned and spat licorice. He was young and black-haired, arrogantly handsome, with lots of strong white teeth. "Worchuk." The name dropped like a brick. "Where's the boss?"

Papa was just coming in from the house. Worchuk's pinch—unexpected, unthinkable—caught me as I turned. He winked at my father. "Say, that's some ripe tomato you've got. Little on the young side, but not bad, not bad." Flushed and humiliated, I waited for Papa to wither the offender. But Papa was smiling, hand extended. I fled to the dry goods and there, kneeling safely behind the counter, listened to the compact. Papa's voice vibrated with unfamiliar heartiness. "You like snuff? Here, take, it costs you nothing. Now, I was saying, you bring your boys in, I fix them up for school—overalls, sweaters, the works. The price is right, I promise. And you don't pay in cash one cent." Steve for his part was playing it cool. "If I deal here, Bruser, it's got to be a fair shake all the way. I bring in butter and eggs, you take 'em, right? And senega root. Last fellow had this store, tried to jew me down—" I saw Papa wince. Worchuk bulldozed on. There was to be a flat price on eggs—"I don't go for that candling and grading. I got good eggs"—and a special discount on hundred-pound sacks of flour. Worchuk was at the door already when he looked at me again.

"You got two girls, Bruser?"

"Yes, this is the baby." Papa's smile was proud. "We have also Cecely, in high school."

Worchuk took my measurements dispassionately. "I got a girl, not so fat as yours, little shorter. Any clothes you don't need, we can use. Your old lady too." The door banged.

After that, we saw a lot of the Worchuks. Mrs. Worchuk (her husband never called her anything but "the Cook") was white as a mushroom and Steve, a swarthy man, was terribly proud of her skin. "Look at that," he said, showing her off to Papa the first time. "She's like that *all over.*" The Cook looked straight ahead with pale, flat eyes. "I bring eggs," she would announce, or "butter." That was as much as she ever spoke. She communicated through her husband or, when he left for the beer parlor, through one of the small brown children who scuffled and clung as she waited for the grocery order. Her butter was unbelievably dreadful, tasting of mice and damp cellars, but Papa accepted it without question. "Why?" he explained. "Because a living I have to make, yes? To Worchuk I don't say 'Your wife makes bad butter.' A temper he has like fire, and friends—the whole district. From such butter one can always make soap."

Whether it was thanks to Worchuk or not, the store prospered. Every Saturday night was a triumph. Even with extra help, we could hardly wait on all the customers who pressed against the front counter, waving their lists. Cecely and I bustled back and forth loading bundles into wagons, Mama manned the cash register. As for Papa, he was everywhere, radiant—greeting, telling his favorite stories, handing out oranges and candy to the children. I suppose he enjoyed the experience of making a little money at last, but his delight went far beyond such mundane satisfactions. He was a community figure, respected and admired; his store had become the meeting place of the district's most prominent farmers; it was *O-Kay*.

With triumph came responsibility. Papa's advice was increasingly sought on financial matters. Mama was consulted on problems domestic and, more surprising, medical. Sometimes I came home from school to find a customer stretched out on the sofa while Mama, frowning, palpated a swollen stomach. Often I was pressed into service to write letters for farmers who signed with an X. There was a steady demand for packaging. One day, just before Christmas, Steve Worchuk appeared with an armload of bundles. "Here, Bruser, wrap these good. They go back to Eaton's." I looked at his purchases. Any one he might have bought at our store, how *could* he ask Papa to handle transactions for a competitor?

But Papa's smile was cordial as ever. "You want different merchandise, or I tell them to send you back the money?"

The first Grandview Christmas came, the deep cold Manitoba winter, and then summer. As harvest drew near, a bumper crop seemed certain. Papa started to make plans for improving the store, and Mama put a new coat of whitewash on the privy. "We're staying," I whispered to Cecely. It seemed too good to be true. The very next night we wakened to a great thumping and banging below. I heard Papa's slippers flapping down the stairs, a burst of voices. Then Mama stood by the bed, the kerosene lamp in her hand.

"Freidele? You're not sleeping, dear? Come, help." Her voice sounded furred and lumpy.

"What's the matter?"

"The Worchuk boy—Alex, the little one. He fell from the tractor—*oy gewald!*—under the wheels. So is now the family downstairs."

I knew Alex—a quick mouse of a boy, always hovering near the cookie bins. I tried to imagine him riding the big tractor, falling, the snap and crunch of wheat stalks all around. Dead. It wasn't real. My face felt stiff, like when the dentist gave me novocaine for a filling.

"But why are they here?"

Mother sighed. It was a sigh that carried with it lament and wonder—wonder at the mysterious ways of the gentile world. "They have tomorrow a big funeral. They come for hats—and yeast."

The hats I understood, but the yeast? Bundling me into my robe, Mama explained. "For a funeral there must be fresh buns. So she makes right away the dough, it should have time to rise."

In the kitchen, Papa was crying. The brandy we kept on

hand for sickness stood on the table. Steve Worchuk, his face a furious red, shook his fist and roared. "God damn it, Bruser, that kid could run a tractor since he was born almost! So one day we work a little late, and this happens! I didn't make him! He says, 'Dad, it's plenty light still. You let me finish—'" Seeing me, he broke off. "Here, you, kid. Take the Cook in and get her a hat."

I knew where the funeral hats were stored. Papa made no attempt to keep up with current fashions in headgear; that department he left to Eaton's. But he had always on hand a large carton of featureless dark straws. I pulled it out and began sorting through. A bonnet with under-the-chin ties; that would be for a child. A panama—no, too large; it sunk deep over the Cook's brows. Here now—a big-brimmed garden party sort of hat. . . . Her moon face registered satisfaction. I squinted doubtfully at a bunch of cherries, preposterously large and glossy, pinned to the brim. "You could take those off," I suggested. She shook her head. I followed her back to the kitchen, a strange humping figure, the loose faded housedress hanging just above the oxfords and ankle socks, and the cherry hat riding high.

Farewells were fervent. Papa, I gathered, had made Steve a present of groceries for the funeral feast. He had given, too, a bolt of fine soft muslin for the little shroud. Steve, exuding a warm steamy brandy fragrance, embraced my mother and shook my father's hand. "You're a real white man, Bruser. I won't forget this."

It was shortly after the Worchuk funeral that we heard the first unsettling rumors. There was going to be a new store in Grandview—modern, self-service, just like in the city. Papa pooh-poohed the reports, but I could see he was worried.

"People don't want they should wait on themselves," he said to Worchuk over the grocery counter. "They come to a store, they want service."

"Yah, you're right," Steve said. He reached for an orange and bit into it, skin and all.

"Anyway, to put up a store takes time," Papa went on. "This year for sure they don't build. Already the ground freezes."

"You ain't heard?" There was a hint of teasing in the question. "They bought Johnson's Hardware. Already hammering, too."

It was true. Within weeks, the new store opened for business. Papa and I walked by one evening after the O-Kay was closed and peered through the plate-glass windows. It was a big store, all right, loaded with new goods. Fluorescent lights, plastic counter tops, a row of shiny help-yourself carts lined up at the entrance. I thought of our old brown store and shivered. Papa was cold too. On the way home, he held my hand so hard that the snow on my mitten caked into a hard lump. "Comes Christmas, we show them," he said. "These new fellows got money for fixtures, sure, but display they know from nothing." "That's right." I tried to sound grown-up and knowledgeable. "There isn't anybody can do Christmas decorations like you."

By December I felt less confident. I couldn't face walking past the Bargain Emporium to see for myself, but reports reached us daily. The new store had put up a giant tree with lights and glass balls (a dazzling novelty in rural Manitoba), and underneath was a pile of surprise boxes labeled with customers' names. Every regular customer got a box. They had an immense cardboard Santa riding across the roof in a sparkling sleigh; they were giving out tickets on a free Christmas turkey. It seemed to me, as we hung our accordion-pleated paper bells and streamers, that the colors were getting a bit thin. Papa had made a new window display—a toy circus—but there were fewer oglers this year. People rushed by, shouting and laughing. There were plenty of clear spaces at the grocery counter. "I think," Papa said, "we let go the extra help. A man has such a family, who needs strangers?"

The last Saturday before Christmas was always a big day in the store. I woke very early and tiptoed down the back stairs. The old black stove was already roaring in the kitchen; Mama had set the table with platters of sweet-smelling cinnamon toast and dishes of sparkling jelly. Papa wiped his lips with a linen napkin and pushed back his chair.

"Boris, sit a while," Mama said. "The customers don't break down the doors."

Papa smiled. "But if they should, I must be there, no?"

There was a tiny silence, and then Mama said, quite carefully. "Steve Worchuk, I don't see him these days. He's been in?"

"The roads are bad—and so much sickness everywhere. Today for sure he brings in the Christmas order."

"I see in the *Jewish Post*," Mama said, as though this were a logical continuation, "is for sale in Churchill a nice little business."

"Churchill!" I was interrupting, but I couldn't help it. I had seen Churchill on the map, a dot poised on the edge of the great blue gash of Hudson's Bay. I imagined us setting out by dog sled to forge a new link in the chain of stores—Eskimos—sealskins—the frozen North. . . . "Oh, Mama, *no!*"

"Rona, what kind of an idea?" Papa spoke reassuringly. "In Grandview we make always a living. So we don't get rich. You lie on the ground, you can't fall down. Come, I want we should be ready before the rush."

But there was no rush. Shoppers floated in and out, picking up small items, and Papa greeted them with torrential enthusiasm. "Package of needles? Sure thing, Mrs. Olsen. The best. You got plenty of thread? Buttons? A nice piece percale, maybe, on special? Here, some candy for the little ones. Christmas toys you don't need?"

Watching Mrs. Olsen escape with her needles, I was ashamed of my shame. He was doing this for us. These people had never seen Papa's face, still and grave and beautiful, when he listened to Jan Pierce singing *Kol Nidre*. They had heard his jokes, but not the tender little stories with which he used to put us to sleep. "Then the bad fairy said, 'Let me have your youngest child, the baby, and I give to you a mountain all of gold.' And the Papa said, 'What good is a mountain all of gold and I have not my heart?'" They had never known his joy and pride at the Passover service—"Oh Lord, Thou hast preserved us and sustained us and brought us to this day"—and his radiant prayer, "Next year in Jerusalem!"

Papa had plenty of time, that day, to straighten piles of sweaters that didn't need straightening. It was late afternoon when I saw Steve Worchuk. He was walking on the opposite side of the street, laden with packages, his face turned away. Papa saw him at the same moment. He put down the turkey-feather duster.

"Let him go, Papa," I said. "He can shop at the Emporium. We don't need him."

Papa shook his head. "This I don't believe. Steve is always my friend. Something is wrong, a mistake. I go to see."

I watched him cross the road, in the chinchilla coat that had lost its plush, the ear flaps of his hat drawn down against the cold. The two men talked a minute, Steve stamping his feet and blowing on his fingers as he shifted the heavy bags.

"He'll be in," Papa said, shaking the snow off his coat. "He goes to get the family." Sure enough, a few minutes later, there was Steve, followed now by the Cook, hatless, and the two older girls. He carried a single, crumpled bag.

"Well, now." Papa's voice was a shade too hearty. "Christmas so soon, and so much always to get. **What** will it be, Steve?"

Steve walked past the dry goods, past the ladies wear and the hardware and the toys. He stood at the grocery counter. "Five pounds of sugar," he said flatly. "And a plug of chewing tobacco."

"That's everything?" I couldn't look at Papa's face.

"Well, no, not quite. I got a exchange here." Steve was fishing in the paper bag. Then he drew something out. "The Cook don't like this hat."

The funeral hat lay on the counter. The black straw, dust color now, was raveling at the brim; the few straggly cherries were split and faded.

Papa seemed bewildered. "You joke."

"No, by God, I'm not joking. This ain't the kind of hat she wanted, and she got no use for it. I want my money back."

"The hat you *charged*, Steve. And how can I take back merchandise has been worn already?"

"*Worn?* I say she ain't never worn that hat, and she ain't

never *going* to wear it. Call me a liar, will you—*you lousy kike!*"

Papa's face split in a clown's tragic smile. Then he walked slowly, like a cripple or a man whose back has been broken, to the cash register and rang up No Sale. "Here," he said, taking out two dollar bills and smoothing them flat on his palm. "Now I owe you nothing. The hat she can keep."

The Cook's pale flipperlike hand reached out. Steve was too fast for her. He snatched the hat from the counter, strode over to the potbellied stove, banged open the door, and threw the hat into the flames. I thought I heard the cherries pop.

We stood still a long moment, watching them climb into the wagon, the Cook blubbering, the children huddled together, and Steve furiously whipping the horses on. Papa put his arm around me. "So who needs them?" he asked of no one in particular. "Money we can't eat, our health we have. And next year—" He looked outside, where our old sign creaked and swung in the bitter wind. "Next year in Churchill, yes?"

THE WINDLESS WORLD

◄──────►◄──────►

I REMEMBER the dog. He was a Spitz, I think, or a mongrel with a Spitzy tail, and he balanced on his hind legs on the cover of the Canadian Primer. There was an old woman, too—I learned afterwards that she was Mother Goose—contained, like the dog, within a sharp black circle. The angle of the old lady's scarf, blown forward with stiffly outthrust fringe, suggested wind, but the world of the figures was windless. The blackish, olive-tinted sky seemed absolutely serene; the meadow flowers, each separate on its tuft of careful grass, were still and perfect as the matching flowers on Mother Goose's gown. What was she saying, her pointing finger outlined against the sculptured scarf? Surely nothing so insipid as "Bow-wow-wow, whose dog art thou?" Momentous as an Egyptian hieroglyph on the door of an unopened tomb, the picture haunted me through all the hours in prairie schoolrooms. It mingled with the smell of chalk dust and eraser crumbs, of crude ink splashed into inkwells by unsteady jug-bearers, of apples and pencil shavings and gum. Perhaps it was only when I left the Canadian Readers, in grade six, that I knew for sure the message frozen on those parted lips. The voice of the reader was the voice of the Union Jack: Be Brave (red); Be Pure (white); Be True Blue.

Every autumn, after Labor Day, we got a new book.

What a moment that was, the crisp stacks of readers lined up at the head of each row as we sat in the approved position, eyes front, hands folded, waiting for the signal: "Take one and pass them back." The sour green binding looked unpromising enough. After Books I and II, with their cover pictures, the Nelson Publishing Company made no further concessions to frivolity. Books III, IV, and V presented a uniform front, a Canadian coat of arms with the lion, the unicorn, and the fought-for crown poised above a shaky maple leaf spray. *A mari usque ad mare,* the banner read. From sea to sea, from September to September, the contents of those books were imprinted on the minds of young Canadians. In the small towns where I lived, there was little competition from other influences. We had no library, no magazine stands (or comic books); the radio was dominated by sopranos and the phonograph required cranking. So I read the readers. All through the years, I have remembered the thrilling stories of Horatius and Robin Hood. Fragments of verses, memorized long ago for the school inspector's visit, have blown about the borders of adult consciousness. "Let me live in a house by the side of the road And be a friend to man." "Those behind cried 'Forward!' and those before cried 'Back!'" Were the Canadian Readers so rich as in retrospect they seemed? I often wondered. And then, in the musty basement of a Winnipeg bookstore, I found them—a full glorious set, Books I to V. Magic casements opening on the foam of faery seas—or windows on a petrified forest? I could scarcely wait to know.

I have gone all through the Canadian Readers now, starting with "Tom Tinker had a dog" and ending with Kipling's *Recessional.* A strange journey. A journey in search of myself, perhaps, but even more in search of the attitudes which molded my generation, and of a long since vanished world. It is easy to criticize the readers. What an extraordinary list of authors, for example: there is no Milton, no Shakespeare except for a snippet from *Julius Caesar* and a scene from *As You Like It*. There is not one song from Blake or Burns or Walter de la Mare. Longfellow, however, is most plentifully represented; so is James Whitcomb Riley. Much of the material is anonymous—for reasons which to the mature judgment seem clear. Imperialists abound. Kipling, Edward Shirley, Sir Henry Newbolt, Canon F. G. Scott blow their bugles mightily.

Children of the Empire, you are brothers all;
Children of the Empire, answer to the call;
Let your voices mingle, lift your heads and sing;
"God save dear old Britain, and God save Britain's king."

And behind them—a formidable array—march battalions of female poets with resonant triple names: Hannah Flagg Gould, Agnes Maule Machar, Julia Augusta Schwarz. Looking now at *The Crocus's Song* and *Christmas* ("Every mile is as warm as a smile, And every hour is a song.") I can understand why I thought, as a child, that poetry must be easy to write.

In prose too, the style of the readers offers some melancholy models. "'Let me get up,' said I, waxing wroth, for reasons I cannot tell you, because they are too manifold." Events are hung in mists of sentimental vagueness. The child who longs to *see* the guests at Allan-a-Dale's wedding is told only that "there were a great many lovely ladies in beautiful dresses." Why was Father Valentine beloved? Because he told "wonderful stories" and taught "beautiful things." When not teaching beautiful things, he sat in his room writing "the kind words which had always made his visits so full of good cheer." What would a third-grader make of the bare statement (in "Pippa") that "A great deed that the world needed must be done, and the man loved the great deed"? How would a fifth grader respond to Lord Avebury's solemn advice: "Time spent in innocent and rational enjoyments, in healthy games, in social and family intercourse, is well and wisely spent"? From diversions like this, a young scholar must have skipped lightly home to the chores.

Illustrations for the Canadian Readers include a good deal of amateurish line drawing, dark blurred photographs, and acres of third-rate academy painting. Sometimes the pictures bear directly on the text, sometimes they are just vaguely related in feeling, as when "Dog of Flanders," about a boy and his dog, is introduced by the painting of a girl and her sheep. Landscape studies predominate, but it is a landscape startlingly irrelevant to the experience of the audience. Apart from some amusing "oriental" scenes, the world of the readers is English: indoors, nannies and beautifully groomed children at teatime; outdoors, a fairyland of stone walls and hawthornes where blackbirds sing from the blooming apple boughs. To the child who rode to school on horseback, past sloughs and wheatfields and elevators, the visions of Rosa Bonheur must have been outlandish as Aladdin.

In addition to being remote, the world of the readers is limited. An adult today is struck by a peculiarly English class consciousness. For example, the account of a rogue named Greene, who led the mutiny against Henry Hudson, begins with a raised-monocle observation to the effect that "this Greene was of respectable connections." Not sur-

prisingly, it's a man's world. The few women celebrated
are those who prove themselves in war the equal of men—
Boadicea, Laura Secord, Florence Nightingale, Edith
Cavell. (There is one essay called "A Pioneer Woman," but
the achievements of its heroine are a sad anticlimax. "Mrs.
Lajimodière was not, of course, expected to carry a load or
to use a paddle, but the journey from Montreal to Pembina
must have been one of great hardship to her. She had often
to pass the whole day seated on the bottom of the canoe."
We are not told whether she carried a parasol.) Even more
serious is the indifference, through all five volumes, to
people of other lands. There is the British Empire, and
beyond that a wasteland inhabited by funny little people
like Oogly the Eskimo and Ning Ting "away over in an
eastern country called China." Japan is a place where
"there isn't a sofa or chair," where one eats without a fork
and rides in neat little rickshaws. You will find "In Japan
that your horse is a man." Not surprising, I guess, to a
child who, in the phonetic tables accompanying Book I,
is given the series "nap, rap, gap, *Jap*." There are Indians
in these stories, but not the Sioux or Cree of any Canadian's
real experience. Gorgeously outfitted in buckskin, they sit
under giant oaks whispering their secrets to squirrels. They
have never seen a reservation, and they have no embar-
rassing Problems.

Perhaps it is unfair to protest, in material for the primary
grades, the absence of any scholarly or scientific spirit.
Still, it does seem that the borders between real and fanciful
might have been more clearly defined. In grade three the
student learns how umbrellas were invented (an elf,
threatened with a soaking, uproots a toadstool) and how
James Watt discovered the principle of steam. He passes,

without change in style or tone, from Robinson Crusoe to Lord Nelson. (I suspect that most little readers found Crusoe the more credible of the two.) Imaginary events are "proved" by the real existence of places named. Allan-a-Dale's marriage? "To this day you can still see the ruins of the great abbey in which it took place." The Pied Piper? "If you go to Hamelin, the people will show you the hill and the river." *Quod erat demonstrandum.* Even historical material is presented with a curious indifference to fact. Florence Nightingale is described as having personally cared for 10,000 sick. We are told how Sir Philip Sidney looked when he offered a dying soldier his last cup of water—but not the name of the "great battle" just fought. Did the teachers of the 1920's fill in the blanks, supply the necessary correctives? Perhaps some did. But in the one-room schools of my acquaintance the teacher, often fresh out of Normal School, was glad if she had time to hear us recite. Anything else was extra and impossible. I don't recall that a teacher ever provided us with the background, say, for the scene from *David Copperfield,* or played the music which was the subject of "The Moonlight Sonata" and with which we were all supposed to be "so fondly acquainted."

"The Moonlight Sonata" offers a shining instance of a Canadian Reader specialty: the sentimental scene. All the ingredients are here—poverty, affliction, simple virtue and the reward it brings. Beethoven, out for a midnight stroll, hears music and sobbing. Entering the "little, mean dwelling," he finds a pale young man making shoes and a blind girl bent over her harpsichord, dreaming hopelessly of the good music she has no opportunity to hear. Beethoven sits down at the instrument. Luckily, it is in perfect tune, or tunes up quickly at the master's touch. ("From the instant that his fingers began to wander along the keys, the very tone of the harpsichord began to grow sweeter and more equal.") Inspired by the young people's devotion—"they covered his hands with tears and kisses"—he improvises a sonata to the moonlight, then dashes home to record the music—not, however, without promising to give lessons to the young lady. (No biographer tells us how often he returned.) Another favorite tear-jerker was "The Lark at the Diggings." Listening to the song of the little brown bird, hardened criminals, exiled to Australia, are reduced to tears. Shaggy lips tremble as the song evokes visions of "the old mother's tears, when he left her without one grain of sorrow, the village church and its simple chimes" and "the chubby playmates that never grew to be wicked."

In order that our chubby childhood might be secure from temptation, the readers lectured us continually. "Teach us to bear the yoke in youth" was the burden of the inappropriately named "Children's Song." "Teach us to rule ourselves alway, Controlled and cleanly night and day." Goodness was a full-time job, *that* was clear. How we marveled at the story of David Livingstone, a perfect lad even before Africa beckoned. "When he swept the room for his mother, there was no leaving of dust in dark corners where it might not be noticed, no dusting round in circles and not underneath." At ten, this paragon earned his own living at a cotton mill: up at five, then fourteen hours at the loom, a Latin grammar (bought with his first earnings) propped at eye level. "It might have been supposed," ran the text, "that after fourteen hours at the factory, David would have been glad to rest or play when he got home at night." But no. Home from work, he hurried off to night school;

home from night school, he pored over his books until
Mother blew out the candle. Of course, "whenever there
was a Missionary Meeting held within walking distance he
was always there." At the looms, too, joining threads, "he
began to weave his plan of service for his Master." And from
all this grueling routine he emerged fresh as a sprig of
Scots heather. "Whenever a holiday came round he showed
what a splendid out-of-door boy he was as well."

Few of us could have hoped to emulate this noble life
—for one thing, cotton mills were scarce on the Canadian
prairies—but we were given plenty of help. Poems, stories,
biographies—all uplifted. There were tongues in the trees,
books in the running brooks, sermons in stones and Good
in everything. Literally. What does the crocus say, deep in
the snow?

> I will peer up with my bright little head
> I will peer up with my bright little head.

giving us a lesson to borrow, that

> Patient today, through its gloomiest hour
> We come out the brighter tomorrow.

Willows demonstrate helpfulness; rabbits, the rewards of
unselfishness. Sunbeams discover that "in seeking the pleasure Of others [we've] filled to the full [our] own measure." Hens are punctual; bees, naturally, industrious; horses
know how important it is to "Do your best wherever you
are, and keep up your good name." If you listen carefully
to the song the whitethroat sings, you will find that it is
a patriot bird: "I-love-dear-Canada, Canada, Canada."
Beavers are introduced early into the business of cutting

trees for the winter, and you know what? "The little fellows found that work was even better fun than play." Over and over again, we are reminded that though intelligence and tender feeling are goods, there is one Good greater far. With the anonymous singer of Book IV, we cheerfully learn to say,

> Head, you may think; Heart, you may feel;
> But, Hand, you shall work alway.

I can smile, now, at the naïve moralizing of the Canadian Readers. It did no harm; perhaps many children profited. But one aspect, one direction, of the material still seems to me pernicious, unforgivable: the exaltation of empire and the glorification of war. Through the whole five volumes, only two selections suggest in any way the virtues of peace. One is about a statue of Christ erected in the Andes, the other a rather pallid account of the League of Nations. Drowning out these faint whispers, the drums of war beat loud. This is a world where little boys dream of battle. "I will try to be very good," says Jackanapes, son of a father killed at Waterloo. "But I should like to be a soldier." His grandfather's old heart swells with pride. "You shall, my boy, you shall." A tale of powder-monkeys, for the third grade, describes the thrill of children on warships "going about [their] work amid the smoke and thunder of the guns, and seeing men struck down beside them by the fire of the enemy." A bit dangerous, of course, "but it was a fine training for the boys." Some of them even become admirals, and in this world making admiral is a big thing. Columbus was an admiral. So was Sir Cloudesley Shovell and Grenville and Raleigh and Drake.

Admirals all, for England's sake . . .
They left us a kingdom none can take,
The realm of the circling sea.

If the kingdom must be won with human lives, that is a
pity, certainly. But the true Briton sees these things *sub
specie aeternitatis*.

Though our only reward be the thrust of a sword
And a bullet in heart or brain,
What matters one gone, if the flag float on,
And Britain be Lord of the Main!

Four years after the close of the First World War, school-
children are invited to admire a battle for the Yser Canal,
"an inferno of destruction and death." Shells burst, flames
cloud the moon, and the great guns roar. "It was glorious,"
writes the author. "It was terrible. It was inspiring." Poet
Laureate John Masefield describes the battle of Gallipoli
in terms which emphasize, ultimately, its dreadful brilliance.
Within hours, he speculates of a departing troop ship, one
tenth of the men "would have looked their last on the sun,
and be a part of foreign earth or dumb things that the tides
push." One third would be "mangled, blinded, or broken,
lamed, made imbecile or disfigured"; the rest would suffer
agonies in the trenches. Still, the little readers are reminded,
"these things were but the end they asked, the reward
they had come for, the unseen cross upon the breast. All
that they felt was a gladness of exultation that their young
courage was to be used. They went like kings in a pageant
to the imminent death."

One can smile, now, at the Canadian Readers. Naïve,

jingoistic, unscholarly, sentimental, moralistic—they were all these. And yet the fact remains that they were also memorable and moving. Few children of this generation will cherish their memories of Dick and Jane. But who could forget Jack Cornwall, the hero of the Battle of Jutland, or Madeleine, the heroine of Verchères? What are Spot and Puff compared with Bruin, the Canadian bear who terrorized a lumber camp, and gentle Patrasche, who pulled a milk cart for love? The world of the readers was a world of heroes. And in the end it didn't much matter, I think, that these heroes were dedicated to purposes which a modern finds questionable—the invincibility of the British fleet, or the glories of empire. What mattered greatly, to all of us who succumbed to its spell, was the vision of men committed to a principle beyond self. I think of Grace Darling, rowing out to a shipwreck through furious seas; of plucky little Pierre, who stole through the German lines to bring news that would save his village; of Captain Scott's last journey, and the dying Oates, who walked out into the blizzard to relieve others of responsibility for his care. In the end, the British Empire became a kind of metaphor—for honor, dignity, unselfishness, and courage. In today's schoolbooks, the captains and the kings depart—and what is left is the kid next door.

Along with the sense of the heroic the readers communicated something equally valuable, a sense of the importance of the individual. Every man *mattered*. Any man might become great. Little Antonio, who carved a lion out of butter for a rich man's table, becomes a famous sculptor; honest Michael, an ordinary Dutch sailor, risks death rather than betray his master and rises "step by step till he became an admiral." Whatever stone you cast into the waters carried reverberations to distant shores. John Cornwall, mortally wounded but still manning a gun, wins "a renown that can never fade so long as men reverence . . . Duty and Honor." The story of Grace Darling's brave deed "was told all over Europe and America. High and low, rich and poor, united to sing her praises and extol her bravery." It is not true, I see now, that Alan McLeod, V.C. "left behind an undying story and an immortal name." (Who *was* Alan McLeod?) But I am glad that I grew up believing in such a possibility.

The vision of the Canadian Readers was limited; it focused almost exclusively on a Protestant, Anglo-Saxon ideal. But it was always a moral vision. Open a modern school anthology and you will be struck with its efficient treatment of man as a social being: here is the real world of real children working, playing, or, as the psychologists would say, interacting. Open the Canadian Readers and you will find an often passionate concentration on what makes a man *a man*. This is true from the very beginning. Consider, for example, the First Reader story of "The Little Blue Egg." A boy, a decent chap really, takes just one peep at the nest, and then—they are *so* pretty—just one egg. The bird will surely not miss it. But at night, the egg safely hidden, he cannot sleep. However deep he huddles into the bedclothes he hears at the window a voice louder than any bird: BRING BACK MY LITTLE BLUE EGG. Compare this with an episode from a modern grade one reader.

> Sally found a big white egg.
> "I will take this," she said.
> "It looks like a ball."

Her brother sets her straight.

> "You funny girl," laughed Dick.
> "I cannot play ball with that egg.
> You must take it to Grandmother."
> Away Sally ran to the house.

Sally has learned, I suppose, a useful lesson. An egg is an egg is not a ball. But it's a far cry from the deep moral shudder communicated by that long-ago tale of the fatal blue egg.

Instead of the familiar—in vocabulary, situation, and scene—the Canadian Readers confronted us constantly with the unfamiliar, the strange. It was not a bad idea. "Sleep, baby, sleep!" runs a poem in the primer. "The large stars are the sheep; The little stars are the lambs, I guess, The bright moon is the shepherdess. Sleep, baby, sleep." Any first grade teacher knows that "shepherdess" is a hard word for six-year-olds—but how nice that we heard it so young. As for the unfamiliar scenery presented in the Academy paintings: we had all seen enough tractors, and one mile of prairie is much like another. The images of orchards and castle walls were not baffling but liberating; they gave us room to grow.

A final observation about the Canadian Readers. Theirs was a world of extraordinary security and joy. The pages shine with birds and stars and flowers. What does the thrush say, little girl, little boy?

> O, the world's running over with joy!
> Don't you hear? don't you see?
> Hush! look here! in my tree
> I am as happy as happy can be.

Minutes later—another page, another poem—he is joined by the chickadee ("Good morning! Oh, who are as happy as we?") and, in *Spring Waking,* by a redbreast.

> A Robin began to sing,
> The air grew warm, and the grass turned green.
> "'Tis Spring!" laughed the Sun, "'tis Spring!"

There are fields and fields of joyful flowers unfolding in the sun:

> "Wake," said the sunshine, "and creep to the light."
> "Wake," said the voice of the raindrops bright.
> The little plant heard it, and rose to see
> What the wonderful outside world might be.

When snow overwhelmed the prairies, blotting out the memory of green, how pleasant to be assured that March's call, "Ho there! Ho!" would be answered by "Ha! Ha! Ha!"

> In a chorus soft and low
> From the millions of flowers under the ground—
> Yes—millions—beginning to grow.

In this best of all possible worlds, snow implied sunshine and rain, flowers. Darkness was an illusion.

> 'Tis always morning somewhere, and above
> The awakening continents from shore to shore
> Somewhere the birds are singing evermore.

Above all, it was a solid, comfortable, ordered universe, where evil was always vanquished and right enthroned.

> Truth shall conquer at the last,
> For round and round we run,

And ever the right comes uppermost,
And ever is justice done.

And what was truth? It was not various and shifting, but a standard clear to rational man. "Teach us," we sang in "Land of our Birth," "The Truth whereby the Nations live." *The Truth*, in capital letters—single, absolute, in all times and places infallible. Perhaps it is this sense which, in the end, makes the intellectual landscape of the readers remote as the Land of Oz. Chicken Little set out, in the primer, to tell the king the sky was falling, but we knew it was only a leaf. For this was indeed the windless world.

How could we have guessed the sky would ever fall?

SHADES OF THE LITTLE
RED SCHOOLHOUSE

ⵈⵠⵗⵈⵗ⬦ⵗⵔ⬦ⵗⵑⵗⵈⵊ

I STARTED SCHOOL when I was not quite five—an early launching inspired by simple necessity. My mother had to work at the store, and there was no one home to look after me. In those days, the age for entering first grade was flexible: you appeared, more or less, when you were ready. Some children didn't feel ready until they turned eight or nine. Since they often left for good at fourteen, their period of bondage was short indeed.

I remember well the day Mama presented me to Mrs. Wiggin, who taught the two beginning grades. Mrs. Wiggin had eyes like apple corers, a lumpy potato nose, and the tight, scoopy mouth of a fish. Her battleship gray hair was twisted into a hard, aggressive topknot. Then and later, she reminded me of Jiggs' wife Maggie in *Bringing Up Father*.

Mrs. Wiggin looked me over. "Too little."

I was short for my age and had not yet grown a proper head of hair. With my baby fuzz and childish smock, I probably did look too little. Mama urged me forward. "Freidele *reads*. The whole first book."

Under Mrs. Wiggin's ferocious eye, I demonstrated my powers. The Little Red Hen, Matilda Jane, The Fox and the Grapes. Luckily she turned the pages for me. (Knowing when to turn the page was the hard part.) It wasn't until weeks later that she discovered the truth: my reading ability scarcely went beyond the letters of the alphabet, but I had a close acquaintance with my sister's old grade one reader. This was the first of many occasions, in Canadian schools, when rote memory made up for higher capacities.

After that I trudged daily to school, where disillusionment set in rapidly. I began eager to master the mysteries of print. Instead, I found myself filling one scribbler after another with the exercises Mrs. Wiggin thought an essential preliminary to writing. First a row of footballs tipped slightly to the right, each outline swirled round and round as if with wire. Then a row of sheaves, straight up and down strokes packed in springy bunches. From these elementary formations we branched out into swirly cats (football over football, with ears and whiskers) and rabbits. In some mysterious fashion, this work was intended to prepare us for cursive script. It was also—like arithmetic later, and Latin, and strapping—"good discipline."

Mrs. Wiggin was very strong on discipline. We could not leave our seats without permission or, except in direst necessity, "go to the basement." Often there was a difference of opinion between teacher and pupil as to the extent of the emergency. These occasions provided welcome diversions. "Mrs. Wiggin, Mrs. Wiggin, Jimmy Ashdown's wet his pants!" The offender would be dispatched for a mop. Meanwhile, girls tittered and boys ostentatiously held their noses, the more histrionic miming an extremity of nausea or distaste. Putting your feet in the aisle, banging a desk top, whispering, passing notes, hesitating too long over a hard word at reading time—any of these minor sins got you a sharp crack on the knuckles from Mrs. Wiggin's wooden ruler. For really major offenses like fighting at recess, the penalty was banishment to the cloakroom or public strapping.

Though punishments figured more prominently than rewards in Mrs. Wiggin's regime, I remember the thrill of her few prizes. Goodness, academic or social, got you a blue star on the chart at the head of the room. Ten blue stars made a red, ten reds made a gold. A month of goodness and you won the right to clap the blackboard erasers together outdoors or carry a note to the principal. I never questioned the value of these distinctions, though I preferred the reward that came with finishing work early —a chance to read one of the books from Mrs. Wiggin's glass-fronted case. Sometimes, too, good children got a mimeographed picture to color—a treat not altogether liberating, since we were expected to use the colors indicated and not go over the lines.

Mrs. Wiggin's regime was stricter than most. Still, that first grade experience provided a useful introduction to school life. As we moved across the prairies, I attended a different school almost every year. Though naturally the quality of instruction varied, those Canadian schools of the 1920's and 1930's seem to me, in retrospect, of one color and mold. Brown walls, green window-shades, alphabet letters marching across the tops of blackboards, a clock, a Union Jack, a photograph of King George V in his coronation robes. . . . The landscape seldom changed. Generally our teachers were raw young Normal School graduates without any university education. One teacher, with pretensions to something she called "culchah," lectured us about two engaging Russians named Lion Tolstoy and Fido Dostoyevsky. It was she too who told us that Boccaccio had written a wicked Italian book called *Da Camera*. In Winnipeg, a high school teacher told us about a famous Greek play. "Remember the name," he said. "Copy it in your notebooks." And turning to the blackboard, he wrote it large and clear. *Oedipus Wrecks*.

As for what we learned—in general, the luxury subjects, music and art, were badly taught. In art the teacher passed out pussy willows and each pupil drew his twig. (Often there was scuffling and argument over who got the best piece.) We worked always from a model, the actual pussy willow or pumpkin and the additional inspiration of the teacher's blackboard drawing. The idea was to be as accurate as possible (right number of pussies) and to work neatly. I remember months devoted to the study of perspective, drawing a box from every possible angle at many imagined distances, using a string to help find the elusive "vanishing point." I remember greeting cards routinely decorated with Christmas holly and Dominion Day flags. Art was copying. And music was singing—all through the grades, the same melancholy corpus of English and Scottish songs. I never learned to read notes. Another "extra," physical training, I associate with regimented drill, usually under the direction of a panting middle-aged teacher in lisle stockings and sturdy oxfords. "Hands on hips, firm! Head to the right, *bend*. Head to the left, *bend*. Stand at ease. Atten-SHUN!" Sometimes we had a brief spin at folk dancing, this too performed in orderly lines, as were most of the games.

Because I was so weak in arithmetic, I am perhaps a poor judge of the training I received. It seems to me, though, that the approach to mathematics was completely mechanical. We were taught rules, not principles. We learned to perform operations, but not to see what the operations meant. *To divide fractions, invert and multiply:* that was magic, not reason. I was taught to count on my fingers—with this additional sophistication. When we grew up, Mrs. Wiggin said, we should make our calculations inconspicuously by resting one casual hand against a cheek. I recall, from second grade, an unfortunate who burst into tears because he could not add a column of three-figure numbers. "It's the carrying," he sobbed. "Show me again." Weary, impatient (she had other grades waiting), our teacher snapped, "Never mind, Bill. If you end up a rich man, you'll have somebody else to count for you. And if you're poor, you won't have anything to count anyway." We all thought that a sufficient answer.

Elementary science taught by lady teachers with a complete lack of equipment almost always turned into botany, and botany into pressing leaves. We drew cross sections of flowers, and sprouted lima beans. Once or twice a year we did an experiment, a great occasion, with the lower grades gathered round to behold the wonders of nature. I remember vividly the experiments themselves, but not what they were supposed to prove. I know, for instance, that when you put a nasturtium into a bottle of red ink, the stem and leaves turn red. I have never found any good use for this information. I was fascinated by the discovery that if you place a piece of cardboard over the top of a full glass of water and invert the glass, the cardboard remains in place—but I thought this marvel had something to do with the qualities of cardboard. Then there was the trick involving three bowls of water—one cold, one hot, one lukewarm. We were all invited to see for ourselves that to a hand recently immersed in hot water, the lukewarm felt cold; if you began with cold, the lukewarm registered hot.

For many years I thought this explained the theory of relativity.

History I loved, partly because it was so orderly (every war had causes, events, results), partly because, as taught in Canadian schools, it was a richly romantic study. British and Canadian history alternated in the curriculum. From Canute to Victoria, from French explorers to Confederation, the story of a nation emerged through its personalities. The past appeared an accretion of splendid moments, triumphs of the human spirit. It was Augustine saying of the young Britons, "Not Angles but angels." It was Alfred burning the cakes while he dreamt victory, Wolfe reciting Gray's *Elegy* the night before his great battle with Montcalm, Bruce and the spider. It was Laura Secord hurrying through the woods to warn the British, Latimer at the stake thrusting first into the flames the hand that had signed his recantation. Events, as we studied them, had an extraordinary one-dimensional simplicity, an absolute morality that survives today chiefly in the TV Western. Britain was good, her enemies bad, her allies and dominions incredibly fortunate in their association. No teacher ever suggested that there was an American version of the Seven Years War, or that the Black Hole of Calcutta demonstrated anything but Indian iniquity. In my last year of high school I happened upon a poem that quite shook me up, a bitter little vision of the Deity's imagined dilemma during World War I:

> God heard the embattled nations sing and shout:
> *Gott Strafe England* and *God save the King*,
> God this, God that, and God the other thing.
> "Good God," said God, "I've got my work cut out."

I think that was when it first occurred to me that God had not written our history books.

Language study, in Canadian schools of that era, had four distinct divisions: reading, spelling, composition, and literature. Oral reading continued right up through high school, a practice inexpressibly dreary for good readers but perhaps helpful to those who needed the spur of public performance. Spelling was lists, rules, and an occasional competition. (In grade four I won the Birch Hills spelling bee. The prize was a new speller.) Composition included grammar, a rigorous formal study with much parsing of sentences. (I recall knotty problems from old examinations. "In the sentence, *That that that is, will perish,* explain the grammatical function of each *that.*") We wrote essays modeled on Addison and Macaulay, whose sonorous prose filled our readers. The strangeness and strain of the resulting efforts may have been due to the fact that Addison and Macaulay never tackled such subjects as "The Diary of a House Fly" or "Making Toffee." Looking now through my battered copy of *English Composition for Secondary Schools* (1930), I am struck by the aridity of topics proposed for sixteen-year-olds. "What a jolly time we had last Saturday!" "Clever Fido." I see also that an alert pupil could have used the same essay five or six times in the course of a year, in response to subjects variously given as "My Funny Mistake," "Out for a Lark," "An Amusing Adventure," "A Funny Story," "A Laughable Mistake," and "An Amusing Experience."

Literature, as taught by the teachers of my acquaintance, became a study in biography and beauty. We began with the life of the writer—an account often, I see now, greatly edited and beautified. The Byron we studied led a spotless life, as did all high-born successful people. Most literary men had titles. We owed our cultural heritage to figures known as the Sweet Swan of Avon, the Sage of Grasmere, the Father of the Dramatic Monologue. When we had copied the Great Life into our notebooks, we proceeded to read aloud, hunt for images, extract noble thoughts and commit them to memory. If a poem seemed specially difficult, we might be asked to paraphrase. Teachers rarely explicated, and students learned not to raise troublesome questions. Once I asked our literature teacher to explain a line from Browning: "Irks care the crop-full bird? Frets doubt the maw-crammed beast?" She managed to look both lofty and withering. "We must not break the butterfly upon the wheel of analysis." The same teacher told me, when I was preparing for the critical eleventh grade provincial examinations, that I needn't worry about the "sight poem," which was a standard feature of the literature test. "Even if you don't understand it," she said, "you can always comment on its felicity of phrase, beauty of thought, and melody of verse." No teacher ever explained what made a thought—or a poem—beautiful. I gathered beauty was the quality common to sunsets, nightingales, and sacrifices like Sidney Carton's far, far better thing. Beauty was a sort of flavoring added to the recipe of a poem. An element, almost a commodity.

I have left non-academic subjects to the last because in some respects they left the most profound impression. Sewing and cooking were taught with extraordinary thoroughness, an emphasis on basic skills. For example, though treadle sewing machines were common during the 1930's, we studied sewing as if no mechanical aids existed. In grade seven, I remember, the year's work was a petticoat.

a project approached as if we had been cast away on a desert island. We were allowed to buy fabric and thread, no more. We made our own patterns out of brown paper. We sewed each seam by hand, executing in the process every known type of seam up to the flat double-felled. We cut and stitched our own bias binding, crocheted our own lace, decorated the neck edge with embroidered flowers of our own design. That no art might be left unturned, we then slit our petticoats down the back and buttoned them up again with hand-covered buttons and handmade buttonholes (some embroidered, some bound). The resulting garment was really too clumsy to be worn. I had outgrown mine, anyway, by the time I tied the last French knot.

In many respects my early education was narrow, repressive, unimaginative. The curious truth, though, is that I *liked* school and acquired there a love of learning. In the long run, some of those hard disciplines proved valuable. Take drill, for instance (now an ugly word). We did a lot of drilling, physical—we were always forming lines and marching—and otherwise. We drilled in arithmetic 2×2, 2×3, 2×4, and on to 12×12, at which point we mercifully stopped. We drilled in geography, shouting out capital cities and products when the teacher called "Alaska" or "Zanzibar." And, oh, how we drilled in languages! In that dim primordial era before the lab and the dialogue, we recited conjugations until our ears rang. *Amo-amare-amavi-amatum:* a branding iron could not more effectively have stamped me with the principal parts. Some of the drill matter was, alas, ephemeral. (What shall it profit a man now that he knows the capital of Serbia?) Some of it was always pointless, like conjugating English verbs. But I can still, at the drop of a comma, tell you the rule for independent clauses not joined by a co-ordinating conjunction.

The Age of Drill was also the Age of Memory Work. I write in capital letters because so clearly these periods have passed into history, like the Neolithic Age or the Age of Steam. In the schools I attended, undue emphasis was placed on rapid in-class memorizing, a terrific strain for children whose minds didn't work that way. Rote repeaters were valued more than truly independent spirits. We spent far too much time copying notes from the blackboard and regurgitating them on examinations. But I am glad I was made to memorize whole scenes from Shakespeare—glad, even, that I had to memorize Longfellow's *Psalm of Life* and the speech of Spartacus to the gladiators at Capua. Those "memory gems" became part of my mental furnishings and, ultimately, a touchstone of value.

A natural outgrowth of memorization was respect for facts. My goodness, what a lot of facts we knew! Time was when I could have reeled off, at a moment's notice, the dates of all the battles in the Hundred Years War, the digestive juices and their functions, the chemical elements and their valences, the parts of a flower and the rivers of Europe in order of size. I could have told you Nelson's words at Trafalgar, and Sir Philip Sidney's at Zutphen. What we did with these facts was often not very interesting. We made lists and charts with them, answered questions when the superintendent visited. But though we did not always use facts as a basis for informed opinions, at least we never assumed it was possible to have valid opinions if we had no facts at all.

Penmanship was a graded academic subject in my day, right up to high school. It was not a bad idea. Granted there was a lot of nonsense in this area. Left-handers were forced to use the right hand. We had copybooks full of hateful perfect lettering which we were expected to emulate down to the last fat swoopy curve of the Capital Z. We were also involved in a passing controversy over the actual physical forming of letters. At one stage, the elegance of our penmanship counted for nothing unless it was the result of vigorous push-and-pull free arm movement. (The teacher moved up and down the aisles, checking. Finger cramp was out.) But over and above these absurdities there shone a single valuable lesson: writing well mattered. Legibility was a virtue, not a sign of conformity.

In addition to writing neatly, we Kept Notebooks. In everything. We had a separate "scribbler" for each subject, and the big thing about scribblers was that you never scribbled in them. You didn't even color in the cover pictures or underline the times tables on the back. Because the notebook wasn't just for you. It was for the teacher (to mark), for your parents (to admire). Almost, we imagined it was not for an age but for all time. So we made headings and underlined in red and used our very best penmanship throughout. The notebooks were collected and checked regularly; all but the most depraved students ended up every year with a model set. I can still remember the lovely satisfied feeling when, cleaning out my desk for the last time in each grade, I riffled through those orderly pages. *Science, History, Geography*. There was a sense— it has seldom come again—as of having truly mapped a strange country, secured a particular segment of knowledge in a comely box. Illusory it may have been, but it entered into my feeling about the joy of learning, the beauty of order.

Our schools were competitive, sternly and openly. Even in grade one, it mattered whether you were a Sparrow or a Bluebird. (The names barely concealed the class structure.) Our report cards listed rank in class as well as percentile scores. Some years—this was *really* pushing it— each child received the same card, a mimeographed sheet listing the marks and rank of every child in every subject. Nothing was said about our charm, our sweetness, our adjustment to the group; the mark was everything. This kind of gross competitiveness must often have been destructive. I'm not sure it was any more destructive than the practice of blurring intellectual distinctions up to a certain point, pretending that grades don't matter—and then suddenly, around grade nine, breathing fire on the subject of College Boards or employer demands.

Because our schools were competitive, they emphasized examinations. These were not quizzes, regular quick canters over material recently covered, but end-of-year grillings which held you responsible for knowing, in June, what had been taught the previous September. Like runners we trained for that final hurdle which would determine whether we moved on to the next grade or—dreadful ignominy—kept our places as "repeaters." Social promotion was unheard of; we moved when we were ready and not before. The price of this rigor was the presence, in most rooms, of certain melancholy figures in the back rows—boys and girls whose legs were too long for the seats, whose awkwardness and uncertainty was emphasized by the briskness of their younger classmates. I cannot think of them without sorrow —and yet I wonder if they were any worse off than the youngsters who, in a modern system—however unprepared, unable in some cases to read elementary materials—are propelled inexorably through the schools by the principle of one grade, one year. What crushes a child more, I wonder—to hold him back until he achieves a certain level of mastery, or to let him go forward without it to a challenge he cannot meet?

Challenge . . . the word comes very naturally to mind in connection with those old-fashioned schools. We had a certain amount of fun, but we never imagined that school was a place you went just to enjoy yourself. School was serious business. Learning was books. I never heard, when I was in high school, about an enriched curriculum—but no wonder. I was studying, in the same year, French and Latin and English and history and biology and civics and chemistry—along with, of course, music and domestic science. We had no study periods in school, and took classes until 4 P.M. We were, in short, sufficiently occupied.

I graduated from high school in 1938, in an Episcopal church banked with gladioli. Members of the girls' ensemble, wearing pastel linen, leaned their heads together and sang Campion's "There is a garden in her face. . . ." The valedictorian recited poems we all knew by heart. "To you from failing hands we throw The torch; be yours to hold it high." *"Play up, play up, and play the game!"*

Two months later, Hitler marched into Czechoslovakia. What we had learned in the schools—about the invincible crown, the rule of reason and the nobility of man—was suddenly in question. Boys from Saskatchewan who had never traveled beyond Regina rode troop trains to Halifax and flew over the cities of the Ruhr. The isolation of the prairies had ended . . . and the sun that set on the British Empire was setting, too, on the little red schoolhouse.

SIGNED WITH
THEIR HONOUR

⋯⋙⟶⟩⬥❂⬥⟨⟵⟨⋯

PROFESSOR ANDERSON first entered my life soon after
I turned seven. That was the year my sister Cecely began
music lessons, creating for me a situation of gnawing in-
feriority. Every day after school she seated herself at the
piano on a little revolving stool and, with much hair tossing
and finger flexing, hammered out something called *Swans on
the Lake*. My parents listened devoutly. I burned. There
seemed, suddenly, much less interest in my perfect reading
scores; talk ran to my sister's future on the concert stage. I
considered asking for piano lessons myself—but Cecely was
off to a head start and anyway, the business of scales looked
dreary. Deliverance came, unexpectedly, when Mama found
in the pages of the *Saskatoon Star-Phoenix* a work produced
by a nine-year-old. "Listen," she said, "how a child writes
poetry.

> Meet things always with a smile,
> You're sure to find it worth while.
> Later on you may be glad
> For being happy instead of sad.

From the reverence in her voice I divined that here was an
art higher even than music. "Mama," I announced the very
next day, "I have an inspiration for a poem." I don't know
where I got the idea that inspiration was involved, but the

effect of this news was magical. "Boris!" Mama called.
"Quick! A pencil and paper. Cecely, please, no more noise
at the piano! Your sister *writes*."

A new era began. Rhyming, I found, was easy. As for
ideas, it appeared that anything—snow, rain, winter, summer, flowers—was a fit subject for poetry. Family love was
especially good. I churned out lyrics to my parents in
general ("To me you are millions in silver and gold, Dia-
monds and rubies and riches untold") and to my parents
on special occasions. Whenever I produced a new poem,
Papa copied it out on vellum stationery and sent it to the
Star-Phoenix. "By Freidele Bruser, Age 7. Certified original,
B. Bruser, Father." My career might have gone on this way
indefinitely had I not, in one leap, removed myself from
the sphere of provincial newspapers and landed on Olym-
pus. Bored with the seasons, I turned to narrative and
rhymed out an Indian love story. The details are hazy to me
now. There was a Great White Trader, I remember (*Trader*
made for hard rhymes, but I managed), an aged chief, and,
naturally, a maiden. The last scene was especially poignant.
"Minnehaha was clasped to the trader's breast As the setting
sun sank in the West. . . ." I read it to my parents in the
kitchen after supper. Mama was so moved that she wept with
happiness, but it was Papa who said, "This we must show to
a *professor*."

The project posed difficulties. We lived hundreds of miles
from the nearest university and had no academic connections. I don't believe we even knew anyone who had attended university. But when it came to the needs of children, my parents were resourceful as well as determined.
Papa made annual buying trips to Winnipeg. Why should
he not, this year, take my poems and present them to the

appropriate authorities? I waited impatiently for his return from the city that November. Usually I assaulted him with, "What did you buy me?" This time I was moved by a seriousness befitting my new vatic role. "Did you find a professor? What did he say?" Papa patted a bulge in his overcoat pocket. "When we get home," he said mysteriously, "you see."

Papa had found the university without trouble. "It is behind the Hudson's Bay store all the time," he announced wonderingly, as if astonished to discover that, unbeknownst to us, Thinking had been going on at the periphery of commerce. "But it is many buildings." He had asked first to see the president, been gently redirected to the registrar, and from the registrar's office to Professor Arnold Anderson, head of the English department.

"Did he read *The Indian Bride?*" I asked.

Papa nodded. "Oh yes, while I am there. I told him you wrote it all by yourself and he said, 'Of that I am sure.' And when he finished reading he said—he said. . . ."

"Yes?" I prompted.

"He said, 'I hope some day your daughter sits in my class'!"

Oh. Only that. He had not suggested publication, then, or immediate entrance into the university. I turned away to hide my disappointment.

"Something else," Papa said. He reached into his coat pocket. "The professor sends you a book. It is about kings, by an English *sir.*"

That is how, like the tap of sword on shoulder, Malory's *Morte d'Arthur* first touched my life. *Morte d'Arthur* is a strange book for the young—strange, and also disturbingly familiar. On the surface knights, squires, and maidens shine, the Round Table celebrates. And yet always in the shadows lurk those baleful truths that a child glimpses from time to time—in a bully's sneer, or the smile of a false friend. The images that haunted me, then as now, were pain-colored: knights grappling before a silk pavilion, the trampled grass stained red; ruined castles where kings lie bleeding from mysterious, unhealable wounds; deep forests, lonely and wild, where a white brachet spells enchantment and a hunting horn rings death. Malory showed me the end in the beginning: Arthur receives, along with Excalibur, the news of the last battle, where he must fall beneath a kinsman's stroke; he wins Guinevere and learns "that of her very beauty shall come the end of hopes." The purity of Galahad remained always unreal, incredible; what I recognized, even then, was betrayal. The Grail vision was romance. Lancelot in the chamber of his liege lord's wife, Nimue using Merlin's own magic to bury him alive—that was life. A sense of tragedy was Arthur Anderson's first gift to me.

As time passed, Professor Anderson was elevated, in our household, to a kind of pantheon, the Apollo-Jupiter of a family mythology. My parents spoke not of "when you go to college," but "when you go to the Professor." I pictured him as a knightly figure—Arthur with overtones of Galahad and Lancelot. In full armor, but with vizor raised (What deep eyes he had!) he presided over the academic Table Round, glancing sometimes at that one empty seat. . . . Though I still wrote poetry, I felt no need to present it to the throne. My place would be waiting when the moment came. I thought it not altogether improbable that Professor Anderson might be following my career in the *Star-Phoenix*, or, after we moved to Winnipeg, on the Young Authors' Page of the *Free Press*. Even in the city I retained my vision of the university's shining towers. I was simple as any squire who ever appeared, barefoot and horseless, at Arthur's court.

At sixteen, I qualified for the university. Would my noble sponsor recognize me on sight? That seemed too much to hope for. Nine years had gone by since my father's pilgrimage—and anyway, Professor Anderson had never seen me. I would need a sign—the book.

The University of Manitoba, in 1938, was not Camelot. I had expected something grand like the Parliament Buildings, with marble and staircases, perhaps even a buffalo or two. I found instead a huddle of shabby structures with a distressingly temporary air, like old warehouses pressed into service. In one respect, though, I was not disappointed. Professor Arnold Anderson did teach First Year English. And yes, I could sign up for his section—plenty of places available. Would he, I wondered, glance over the list of names before class? Fed on the recognition scenes of old romance, my imagination blazed.

I took my Malory to the first meeting of English One, and I sat in the front row, beneath the lectern. Students drifted in and out, an irreverent lot, full of loud talk. At the back of the room, one raucous group had a card game going. A girl carried knitting. Someone poked a head in the door and called, "Whose is this?" and someone else said, "Anderson," and the head said, "My God!" and vanished. At ten minutes after the hour the room remained half empty; no lecturer had appeared. At quarter past, a card player announced happily, "We can go!" And then, in the doorway, I saw Arnold Anderson.

He was not Arthur, or Lancelot, but Merlin—a small, stooped, crumpled little person in chalk-dusted academic gown. His face, except for the high aquiline nose, had an almost feminine delicacy. His hair floated like dandelion fluff, and his eyes were sherry colored. He did not stand clear of the lectern, like the young chemistry professor; nor did he grip it like the history instructor, an arrogant young Rhodes scholar who had seemed ready, almost, to hurl it at us. He leaned on the podium, head bowed, and spoke as if to an invisible audience. "We are here," he began, "to explore together the glorious heritage of our literature." In the back row, someone released the cord of a window shade and it clattered to the top noisily. Professor Anderson talked on. We would begin with Shakespeare, and we must be very sure to purchase the Oxford and Cambridge edition, "a volume," he explained, "purged of impurities and dross." The card-playing crowd had a good time with that phrase. I wrote it carefully in my notebook. So far the great man sounded disappointingly like Maud Forester, B.A., my high school English teacher. Could it be that he spoke in a code comprehensible only to the elect? I copied it all down. "Genius defies analysis. It is the fairy's kiss, the sacred fire. . . ." Perhaps in time these dry pods would burst open, revealing the live seed.

The hour bell set off a stampede. Professor Anderson remained quietly at the lectern, shuffling notes into a morocco folder. When he became aware of me at his elbow, there occurred no lightning flash of interest, only a wearily polite, "You wished to speak to me, young lady?"

I longed for a cloak to cast off dramatically. Instead, I placed my *Morte d'Arthur* on the lectern and announced nervously, "Well—you see—I'm Freidele Bruser."

"Yes?"

In all my hectic imaginings, I had never imagined having to explain myself. "You once said . . . I sent you some

poems . . . This is the book you gave me. . . ." Worse and
worse. He was certainly interested now, but it was the interest of stupefaction. I tried to prompt his memory in the
matter of *The Indian Bride*. He coughed, embarrassed for
us both. "Well, it sounds delightful, I'm sure. But you see,
rather a lot of people came to see me in those days—I was
head of the department, you know. I just don't recall a
child. . . ."

"Oh, no!" I interrupted. "I didn't come myself. My father
brought you the poems."

He snapped his fingers. "My dear girl—did your father
wear a high fur hat? I believe I do remember. A striking
fellow, foreign. And I sent you a book, did I?" He laughed,
pleased at the recollection of ancient courtesies. "Really, this
is an extraordinary reunion. You must come to dinner and
meet my wife. She has always been interested in students,
and we see so few young people nowadays. . . ."

And so, after all, the quest was fulfilled, though with the
strangeness and sadness that so often accompany a realized
dream. I had thought of Professor Anderson as the hero who
would lead me into the innermost sanctum of knowledge. I
found him wandering without a kingdom, and now he leaned
on me. Gradually the picture emerged. He had taken his
master's degree before the turn of the century; his thesis, he
told me, explored "The Beauty of Tennyson's Women." In
the early days of the university, when Manitoba was still
primarily an agricultural college, he had shone as a scholar,
with power in his limited sphere. The world, the college, and
the students had long since pushed past him. A brilliant
young man, brought in as head of the English department,
gave courses in the new criticism. Instead of his once famous
Browning seminar, Arnold Anderson now taught beginning

work in composition. Perhaps his mind had slipped a little. More likely he had always been vague, and now to vagueness was added physical weariness and humiliation. At any rate, his demeanor in the classroom was pitiable. He knew that students were bored, contemptuous, indifferent. So he talked in whispers, reading from old lecture notes and waiting for the ordeal to end. I must have been his first prótegée in a decade.

Of course my parents inquired about "the Professor." Did I talk to him? Did he like my compositions? How could I tell them what really went on during those dreadful class periods? They would never have understood that a professor with an M.A. degree could be utterly without power to enlighten. (When we studied *Antony and Cleopatra*, he dictated summaries of the action, scene by scene. Someone asked the meaning of "boy my greatness in the posture of a *whore*" and he flew into a sick, trembling rage.) It is hard to know, at this distance, whether ignorance or kindness led him to praise my essay on "The Poetic Style of Euripides." (I had analyzed Gilbert Murray's translations, unaware that they were translations. Did Arnold Anderson too imagine that Euripides wrote English?) Most of the other students gulled him mercilessly. They interrupted with, "Can I go to the lavatory?", worked openly with compasses and protractors during English class, turned in essays cynically copied out of standard reference texts. One afternoon—he was reading the balcony scene from *Romeo and Juliet*—a group of boys heckled until he burst into tears. I carried his books down the corridor that day. Neither of us spoke. When we reached his office he said, "I wasn't always a tedious old man," and I said, "I know."

In class, I was the only one who answered questions, took

notes, and tried to head off the noisy distractions of back-row rebels. After class, often, Professor Anderson took me upstairs to the faculty common room and there, over tea and thin pale ice cream biscuits, he planned my career. I would major in Victorian literature. "I want you to have my files," he said. "And some day, my books." After Manitoba, I must go to Toronto, where one of Anderson's friends still directed nineteenth-century studies. "Wilson's from the old school," he said. "A true scholar and a gentleman. Not like these pushy young Americans who are coming across the line and turning universities into paper factories." Privately I shuddered at the vision of a future dominated by old-school gentlemen. Still, such attention was not to be sniffed at. Few students ever entered the faculty common room; I had become a regular visitor, introduced around with flattering deference. Sometimes the falsity of my position troubled me. I did not want to be thought of as this man's disciple. On the whole, though, the relationship seemed equitable enough. Professor Anderson was launching me, a raw country girl with an untidy immigrant background. In return, I protected him from the knowledge of his diminished status.

I might have gone on indefinitely, protecting Arnold Anderson, if it hadn't been for Hochstein. His first name was Jacob, but no one ever called him that. He was Hochstein, or Hoch, or the *Wunderkind*—already, at eighteen, a legendary figure. Where most Jewish students moved cautiously, seeking distinction only through academic success, Hoch blazed. His father owned a Socialist book store; his mother, a survivor of the Triangle Shirt Factory fire, was that rare creature in provincial Winnipeg, a professional female labor organizer. Every inch his parents' son, Hoch argued with teachers—a thing unheard of—and had been thrown out of history class for calling the instructor a fascist. He cut lectures (seldom showing up before noon, and then with a hangover), slept with *shiksas*, gentile girls, read omnivorously—but never the books required—and fought for causes. One week he crusaded for a boycott of Japanese silk stockings, the next against the fraternity system, or the notorious Jewish quota in medical school. His *bons mots* circulated widely in the girls' locker room, where we thrilled to his vulgarity. "Did you hear what the *Wunderkind* said about Betty Grable?" I thought him repulsive and fascinating, and naturally I was flattered when, one day in the cafeteria, he sauntered over to my table. "Say," he began. (Hoch had no small talk.) "What do you make of *The Waste Land?*"

"I haven't read it."

"Aren't you taking English One? Well, what in the hell are you doing in modern poetry?"

"W. H. Davies," I said. "And we're going to read some Rupert Brooke."

Hoch stared. "You're kidding. Rupert Brooke, the fair-haired warrior, for *modern poetry?* Tea and crumpets? Whose section are you in, for God's sake?"

When I told him, he threw up his hands and rolled his eyes in a silent parody of "Oy vay's." Then, with the zeal of an apostle who senses fresh convert material, he moved in. "You could get into Bartlett's class. The man's a marvel. Mind like a razor blade. And he's got something to *say*. Everybody knows Anderson's over the hill."

"Professor Anderson's been very kind to me," I said. "I couldn't leave him."

"Christ, what is this—a university or the Golden Age Club?" He shrugged, rose to go, and then, with diabolical casualness, added over his shoulder, "Some showing you'll make on the final exams with *that* kind of preparation."

He had my number. The temptations of wit and learning I might resist, but grades were another matter. At the University of Manitoba, marks depended entirely on a final examination, set not by individual instructors but by an outside committee. Was it possible that Professor Anderson hadn't even assigned the required material? Sentiment might well cost me a scholarship. "Wait a minute," I said. "I'll go to class with you today—just to see what Bartlett's like. Of course, I'm staying in Anderson's section."

"Of course," he said. "Naturally."

So I went with Hoch and heard Ogden Bartlett read the first poetry that ever moved me deeply. It was Spender's "I think continually of those who were truly great, Who, from the womb, remembered the soul's history Through corridors of light where the hours are suns, Endless and singing. . . ." I was accustomed to hearing poetry read with what was called "expression," marvelous lifts and lowerings of the voice, with maybe an occasional gesture for emphasis. Bartlett read in a dry, ascetic monotone but with a luminous delicacy of phrasing, his face a mask suggesting mystery and pain. (Not for nothing was he called Ogden Agonistes.) I'm not sure, now, that I understood what the lines were about. Only I had the impression of dazzlement. Words rang like coins in a fountain of bright water, light streamed about me in a chime of colors. "Born of the sun they travelled a short while towards the sun, And left the vivid air signed with their honour."

"You can speak to him after class," Hoch whispered. "He has to sign the change-of-section slip."

What a despicable fellow, I thought. Not an ounce of

feeling. I scribbled on the back of my notebook (Bartlett was speaking now, analyzing a line with surgical precision): "I don't have to change sections. I can stay with Anderson and sit in on B's classes." "You've got that kind of time to waste?" he wrote back. "Don't be a drip." At the end of the hour I asked Bartlett for permission to transfer. He signed without looking at me.

So. Now I need only find some plausible story for Arnold Anderson and that, given his unworldliness, should not be difficult. I found him at his desk.

"What a happy surprise!" He rose to move a briefcase from the unoccupied chair. "What about a spot of tea in the common room, eh?"

"Oh, I'm sorry, I can't possibly," I said. "I've got a terrific amount of work piled up."

"My dear"—his voice was concerned—"are you sure you're not overdoing? Seems to me you're looking a bit peaked."

"I'm fine, just fine." I plunged on. "But I've run into a scheduling problem. My math section's been changed—and that means I can't manage your ten o'clock English class. I'm afraid I'll have to transfer."

"Why, there's no need to worry. I can speak to your mathematics instructor. That's Professor Reed, is it not?"

"No, no, I don't want you to speak to him. I mean, I really prefer the ten o'clock math section."

"Well, then, I'll just move you into one of my afternoon classes." He took out his ledger and began turning pages, moistening a finger with saliva.

I felt my resolve weakening. Then I thought of Hoch and Bartlett. Born of the sun, they travelled a short while towards the sun. . . . "My afternoons are all filled up." I handed him the poisoned chalice. He took it, knowing it poison.

How many afternoons had I taken tea with him in the common room?

"I see." But he didn't, not quite. He reached for the change-of-section card and studied it briefly. "Ah, yes. Professor Bartlett. A remarkable young fellow, brilliant." He rose then, straightening the front of his robe with a familiar, fussy gesture. "Well, I shall miss you. I hope you'll still come to dinner? My wife has often reminded me—but you know how forgetful I am."

"I'd love to." This was more comfortable ground. "I'll keep in touch, of course. And thank you . . . for everything."

I was partway down the corridor when he called after me, and I turned.

"Miss Bruser—you mustn't be disappointed if Professor Bartlett doesn't notice you at once. He's a young man, you know, with his own way to make."

Arnold Anderson was right. Bartlett did not notice me, then or ever. But I was moving forward. Hoch invited me to join the Morons, an exclusive club where campus intellectuals read poetry and listened to music with important frowns. I won the English literature prize for an essay on the modern temper. One day I received in the mail a note from Mrs. Anderson, inviting me to lunch. I would have gone, but the date was too close to examination period. Avoiding Professor Anderson in the halls was easy; he was notoriously myopic. As it happened, he became ill a few months later and his classes were taken over by a retired army major. I thought how wise I had been to get out in time. When he died, I attended the funeral—a rather handsome gesture of respect, considering my crowded schedule. It was only afterwards, jolting home on the bus, that I thought of Merlin and Nimue and how, when the old enchanter had communicated to her all his secrets, she rolled over him that massive stone.

ONE OF US

⋯⋯⟫⟶⟪⟩⟶⟨⟫⟶⟪⋯⋯

IN A well-regulated universe, great revelations would be heralded by a sign—a star in the East perhaps, or an angel with flaming sword. But to me they have often come unsung. Who, knowing Moishe Bloch, would have supposed him to be the agent of epiphany?

It was 1941, my third year at the University of Manitoba. Although the war too was then in its third year I had, by some marvel of obtuseness, remained largely unaware. The war was not my business. *My* business was study, pursued with single-minded passion. It would be nice to say that I was driven by pure devotion to learning—nice, but not true. My parents had come from Russia with no money, little schooling, and a great hope for the future. Here, in the new world, the children would thrive. What did it matter if the *Mama* and *Tata* worked hard in a country store? Everything was for the children—the breast of chicken, the softest shoe leather, the finest education. First in class, at school and then at the university, we would enter the promised land. I never inquired what one did there. And so I studied to win scholarships, won scholarships so I might continue to study, and asked no questions as the wheel went round. In this curiously mindless, directionless scholarship, I was not unique. Jewish students, children of first-generation immigrants, dominated the prize lists in those days. They were not all of one stamp. There was always, I remember, a small core of intellectuals who followed their own stars in defiance of course requirements and exams. They were to be found in the dim cafeteria, arguing about Nietzsche over cold coffee, or in the music room, where a wheezy phonograph cranked out Beethoven's Ninth. These people did well, but never gloriously. A far larger group, to which I belonged, consisted of the professional prizewinners. Our fathers were junk collectors or proprietors of little country stores, our mothers sent bagels and loving prayers at exam time, and we were driven, all of us, by a single, simple urge: to succeed. Success involved attending classes faithfully, taking copious notes, reading all the commentaries, memorizing key passages, analyzing old exam papers, and never, never allowing oneself to be diverted by irrelevant considerations like "What does it all mean?" One year I took a course in the philosophy of Kant. I found it unbelievably dull. Was this the book that launched a thousand speculations—this collection of bloodless theorems? I committed to memory not only great swatches of *The Critique of Pure Reason*— that was obvious—but also of the leading critiques of the *Critique*. The day of the final exam, as I stood biting my nails outside the judgment room, I was accosted by one of the *real* intellectuals, a hot-eyed young fellow named Tevya. Tevya had missed most of the lectures, was reputed to be in the professor's bad books. "Well," he said, with a heartiness inappropriate to the condemned, "Have you made up your mind about Kant?"

"Made up my mind?" What was there to make up one's mind about? You remembered, or you didn't remember.

"*You* know. . . . Have you decided whether the world's your show, or whether you're the world's show?" He sauntered on, not dreaming that he had just flung open a door. So *that* was what Kant was all about! Why, in that case . . . But the proctors were signaling. This was no moment to think about Kant. I tore to my seat, turned over the question paper, and began to write. I never thought about Kant again. That year I added the philosophy prize to my honors; Tevya, I believe, failed the course.

By the end of 1941, a sense of the war had reached even the most disengaged scholars. France had fallen; Germany was driving forward in the Balkans and in North Africa. Uniforms were everywhere. Some boys had left the university and joined up; those with unsatisfactory grades had been forced to leave. I was riding the streetcar to school one day, at the beginning of the examination period, when I saw Moishe Bloch edging his way towards me. I hunched into my book, prepared to freeze him out. Moishe was one of those pathetic hangers-on who is propelled through an institution of higher learning by no desire of his own, only by the absolute determination of his parents. Weak, soft, easygoing, he would have been happy, I think, to be a pants presser, as his father had been before luck and some canny investments placed him at the head of the Bloch Garment Factory. Moishe had scrabbled through two years of university work with the help of tutors and summer sessions; still carrying "supps"—supplementals—from the previous term, he was not likely to last much longer. Now he breathed strongly in my ear, his foolish face thrust close to mine. "Listen," he said, "I got to talk to you."

I couldn't imagine why. "Excuse me." I kept my eyes on the page. "I'm studying. I have an exam this afternoon."

"Look, please, is important. The Army, it's out to get me for sure. . . ." He made a small noise, something between a groan and a belch. I tried not to smile, imagining him snugly buttoned into an army tunic, shivering in the front line (did armies still fight in lines?) or parachuting down from a fighter plane, his great quivering buttocks looming over Tunis or Sidi Baran. "Sorry," I said crisply. "I don't have any influence with the Army."

"No, no, you don't see. . . ." He really was unbelievably thick. "It's my English. I have next week to make a paper on *Lord Jim*. No paper, I'm through, washed out, *kaput*. And my father—if I go overseas, it kills him, such a heart condition he has. Look, I know English is for you no trouble. Write me a paper. Whatever you say, price no object."

I can't say I felt virtuous indignation. Mostly I was just annoyed. Moishe Bloch never courted my favors when a fraternity formal was coming up. (Not that I'd have cared to go with *him*, anyway.) And now here he was at exam time, bothering me with his problems. "I don't write papers for pay. Anyway, I've got four exams myself next week. I need every minute." The streetcar had stopped outside the arts building. I pushed past him and headed for the exit.

At lunch that day, the table buzzed with scandal. "What do you think of old Rosen?" my friend Hannah asked. "He was caught cheating on the history exam." She made a sharp clacking noise and drew her finger across her throat.

I unwrapped my sandwich and peered inside. Salami. Ugh. "How'd he do it?"

"Played sick and got permission to go to the washroom. They sent a proctor to check, and there he was with his text open, reading like mad."

"Serves him right."

"Oh, I don't know." Hannah was a softie. "I feel sorry for

him. Plenty of kids cheat and get away with it. It's the dumb ones that get caught."

It was on the tip of my tongue to tell her about Moishe Bloch. She'd have been interested. But Hannah was still talking. "Everyone shaves a point some time, one way or another. Haven't you, *ever?*"

I grinned. "Cheat? What for? Who would I cheat *from?*"

"Pardon me. I forgot. Well, lesser minds are not so immune to temptation."

"No, seriously. What Rosen did is—well, it's a contradiction of everything a university education should mean. I don't have any sympathy for people like that."

I thought about Moishe again on the way home. I was changing streetcars at Portage and the Mall, and Hudson's Bay had an all-red window. There were red sweaters, red coats, and—dead center—a brilliant red jersey dress that knocked your eye out. It was the kind of thing worn by Heather Sanderson, whose father donated some of the scholarships I slaved for. I imagined myself swinging down the university corridors while heads turned. "Is that *Bruser?*" If I were the kind of person who wrote papers for money, I could have a dress like that.

I wasn't really surprised when the phone rang that evening. "It's a boy," my landlady said, handing me the receiver. From the sound of the breathing, it must be a whole regiment of boys—a whole family, anyway. Bet they were *all* gathered round. "Look," Moishe began, "I'm sorry what I said this morning. I mean, I know you don't do anything is not kosher. All I want is you should tutor me."

"*Tutor* you? At this stage of the game?" I'd done a certain amount of tutoring during the term—seventy-five cents for a generously interpreted hour—but exam time was different.

"Well . . . look at it like this. I have to write a paper on *Lord Jim*. So you tutor me in *Lord Jim,* and then I write the paper. Everything above board, yes? You name the price."

I hesitated. It wasn't the most above-board proposition I'd ever heard. On the other hand, it wasn't exactly dishonest either. If I worked Moishe over for one solid evening, I might really get him in shape to write his own paper. The red dress was ten dollars. I gathered up my nerve. "Would an evening's tutoring be worth ten dollars to you?"

Over the wires, Moishe leapt to embrace me. I could see the happy flush, the eager eye. "Perfect, perfect! You got yourself a deal. So when should I come?"

A new misgiving shook me. "You *have* read *Lord Jim?* Because if not, the deal's off."

The voice oozed and bubbled. "Sure, sure, how should I not read it? But it's a hard book, *you* know. Some things I could use a little help."

Next evening, Moishe sat across the table from me. He had brought his copy of the novel (very clean), a notebook, and a freshly sharpened pencil.

"Now, just to get started," I said briskly. "Suppose you tell me what you think *Lord Jim* is all about. What's the central theme of the book?"

He smiled happily. "Well, Conrad was attempting to illustrate in Jim's weakness and strength the mystery of human character and to reveal the hidden springs of human conduct. He shows . . ."

After the first sentence, with its manifestly un-Blochian cadence, I couldn't believe it. *Masterplots.* I'd have guessed

anyway, but as it happened I'd taken a look at *Masterplots*
that very day, to refresh my memory on details. The liar,
the vermin, the unspeakable fraud. "You haven't read *Lord
Jim!*" I shouted. "Not a line. You've memorized a crib!"

Moishe looked hurt and sad. "I couldn't help it. Such a
big book, and I read slow. But you help me now, and I
read it this summer, I promise."

"I don't give a damn about your promises!" If I turned
him out now, as he deserved, I lost the ten dollars *and* a
precious evening of study time. I am in blood stepped in
so far. . . . "O.K." I made up my mind. "We're reading it
now, together."

He paled. "The whole book? But I need by next week
the *paper.* . . ."

"No, of course not the whole book! Just key passages.
We'll look at the most important parts, and I'll fill in the
rest. Here—" I opened my copy, with its precious under-
linings and marginal scribbles. ("Cf. Hardy," "N.B. Conrad's theme of illusion," and so on.) "Start reading."

It was awful, far worse than I could possibly have
imagined. "Dogged" in "dogged self-assertion" he pronounced as if it were connected with the canine world. He
did not know the meaning of *aggressive* or *immaculate,*
thought *humane* was synonymous with *human.* He did not
even, it appeared, know what a parson was. (*"Parson?*
Yeah, sure, I know. *Parson, person*—same thing.") Irony
escaped him entirely; no question of attempting illumina-
tion there. I drove him furiously through the opening account of the parsonage from which Jim had come. "Now,
what is the point of this description?" I prompted. "Why
do we need it?" Moishe beamed, anxious to please. "We
don't." At nine o'clock I gave up.

"All right," I announced tightly. "We can't possibly get through the book this way. We'll take another tack. You decide on a topic for your paper, and I'll talk about *that*. And"—I tried to sound casual—"you can take notes."

Rapturous, a spirit released from Hell, Moishe closed *Lord Jim* and consulted his notebook. "I have here a list . . ."

"'Conrad's View of the Nature and Fate of Man,'" I read. "That's fine. We'll do that one."

He shook his head. "Never. This is the second time already I'm failing this course. Bartlett knows on such a subject I can't possibly write."

"This paper is for Bartlett?"

"Yeah, sure. What difference for who?"

It made a lot of difference. I didn't specially mind putting something over most members of the English department —the young men who courted popularity by turning classes into bull sessions on sex, or the old men who riffled wearily through their notes, reading interminably from Legouis and Cazamian. But Bartlett was God—a true original, aloof, inscrutable, omniscient, the one teacher whose good opinion mattered. How could I foist on him this shoddy deception?

From the cover of Moishe's book projected a long envelope with my name on it. I turned back to the list. "How about *this* one? 'The Style of Joseph Conrad.'" Somewhere I'd read a good article on that. I could probably reconstruct without too much trouble . . .

"Uh uh. That he never would buy. The way I see it, there is here only one subject my speed. 'What *Lord Jim* Means to Me.'"

Of course. A perfect duffer's topic. The sort of thing no really good student would touch. I reached out for this soiled undergarment of a subject, anxious to cloak it with the familiar folds of critical drapery. "Conrad's great novel strikes a familiar chord in the heart of every sensitive reader. Jim's pathetic romanticism, coupled as it is with the fatal habit of thinking too precisely on the event . . ." I stopped. Moishe's pencil had, after the first few yords, stopped scratching. He looked sick. "Nah," he said. "This ain't me. It's got to be—you know—what this story says to a plain schmo. Like what has *Lord Jim* got to do with Moishe Bloch?"

What indeed? Come to think of it, what did *Lord Jim* have to do with me? I had read the novel carefully, several times, underlining and annotating. I had committed to memory Stein's great speech on men and butterflies—"A man that is born falls into a dream, like a man who falls into the sea. . . ." I had distinguished myself on the final exam. But the truth of the matter was that *Lord Jim* had never meant anything to me—except, perhaps, a test of mastery. Moishe's querulous interruption caught me, blinded, in a spotlight of cold brilliance. I felt myself rocking, a small, badly rigged ship, on an ocean of immense significance. A phrase from the novel echoed hollowly: "In the destructive element immerse . . ." I jumped.

"You see . . ." I began. What was he to see? What did *I* see? The waters moved. I was Lord Jim, deep in the hold of the doomed ship, holding my lantern to the bulging bulkhead. Any minute now the ocean would overwhelm me. "It's like this. Jim is such a decent fellow, really. He wants to be good, and he thinks he *is* good. He's one of us." Moishe looked up questioningly. "I mean—well, *you* have certain ideas about what you want to do, or be— and I do—and we try to live up to those ideas." Moishe nodded, frowning a little. I felt sudden compassion, thinking how hard it must be for him to pursue his parents' dream. "So we move along like Jim, always getting ready for the big moment when we can prove ourselves. And we feel secure, like Jim that night on the *Patna,* with the big ship sliding over the quiet water, the charts all laid out so neatly, with the compass and dividers and the straight pencil line marking the course. But all the while danger's coming. There's black smoke pouring from the funnel, and the wheel chains grind. Everything explodes all of a sudden —you know, like water at the back door when you're braced for fire at the front—and there's not time to get your hero suit on. You don't think or anything. . . ." Moishe was watching, round-eyed, now. "You just *jump.* And then you don't ever understand what happened. Did you jump because somebody told you to? Because, deep down, you're the jumping kind? Was it just bad luck that you found yourself on a sinking ship, or did you, somehow, go out and *find* that ship, the way Jim found out the *Patna* when he could have gone back to the home service?" I was talking faster now, with a kind of thick excitement, and at the same time ashamed of my excitement. Good Lord, *I* wasn't on trial. I was just helping a fellow with a paper. But the book had taken hold.

Moishe's question came as from the depths of myself. "So what's the answer?"

"Don't you see, there *isn't* any answer, ever? We're always in a mist—'at the heart of a vast enigma,' Conrad says. But every time we fail our dream, we become less able to realize it next time. At the end, when Jim practically delivers his friends to a crook, it's because he has this crookedness in himself."

Moishe sighed, a balloon slowly sputtering out. "I didn't know it was such a sad book."

"Sad?" I was startled. "Well, I guess it is. If you care about being good, you always find out you're not good enough. And somehow, knowing that, you've got to pull your torn coat about you and stand as straight as you can."

I don't remember saying good night to Moishe. He left the envelope with my check in it, and word came by the grapevine that Bartlett was pleased with the paper. I bought the red dress. But the first time I tried it on, the wool itched terribly; another time, I stood turning in front of the mirror and it seemed that the dress made me look fat. Months passed. I heard that Moishe Bloch had been taken by the Army, and felt a kind of mean relief. So I hadn't done anything after all. . . . Still the red dress hung at the back of the closet. At the end of the year, I crumpled it up in a box of old clothes and gave it to the Salvation Army.

THE SILK UMBRELLA

SNOW FELL in May the day my father died. I had
expected, really, not to care; he had been such a long time
dying, and the manner of his going shadowed us all. Was
it ten years before that he began to drift away? It is hard
to say exactly, we paid so little attention. Not that we
didn't love him. But ours was a matriarchal household,
intensely female. "You are the captain," my paternal grandmother told my mother after the wedding. It was that way
from the beginning. Mother made the decisions, charted
the course; my sister and I sat on deck, planning how to
amuse ourselves at the next port and admiring the view;
and my father kept the engines running. No, even that
is not the right metaphor. He was never good with things
complicated or mechanical. On a ship he would have kept
the decks clean, the paint sparkling. And no task would
have seemed to him menial if it contributed to our comfort. He felt himself privileged to serve.

My father was an infinitely gentle man. When I see
him—as I do often, now that the death of that sad invalid
has liberated my true, my real father—it is always in the
posture of tender protection. What was it Hamlet said of
the dead king? "So loving to my mother That he would
not beteem the winds of heaven Visit her face too roughly."
My father was like that. If he could have carried us through

the world on his shoulders, he would have done so. One of the few conflicts of his life, I think (he was a man simple and straight, not vexed by division), was the pull between the desire to give us everything and the need to keep us safe.

"Papa, I want a cap gun!"

"What for, darling? You should hurt yourself?"

Scornful, impatient, I stamped my Buster Brown shoes (oxfords, for the sake of my arches). "You can't get hurt with a cap gun. Everybody else has one!"

So I got my pistol, and the little red roll of paper caps to carry. When the moment came—wait until Sammy Horton sees *this!*—I handed Papa the weapon and he fired. For Halloween, he scooped out the thick-ribbed pumpkin, carving its features with a pearl-handled knife, and through the dark streets he swung the jack-o'-lantern lit with its candle flame. I skipped beside him, a broadcloth witch, collecting candy that Papa would next day distribute to other, less exquisite children. (Who knew, after all, where such candy came from, how it had been handled?) In winter he longed for me to skate—a healthful exercise, and with friends—but there was danger to consider. What if I should turn my ankles? Or, God forbid, fall? He met the problem by ordering a special pair of skate boots with laced inner supports and metal outer clamps to brace my ankles. Toqued, mittened, muffled, cocooned in wool, I shuffled across the ice, flinging myself periodically against the walls of the rink for balance. And beside me in galoshes, an ocean liner among the darting tugs, ready for rescue or for praise, my father.

No single word will conjure up the quality of my father's generosity. It was not permissiveness: a feeling for what one did and did not do was strong in our household. It was not indulgence in any ordinary sense. I think of it, rather, as a special sensitivity to need. When, as a child, I waked crying because the dark got in my nose, he was beside me in an instant. Then he would light the lamp and sit at the foot of the bed, singing softly:

> *Lule, lule lulinke*
> *Shlof nu shlof meyn meydele,*
> Sleep now sleep my little girl,
> *Ah, ah, lulinke,*
> *Lule, lule, lulinke. . . .*

When I wriggled about, unable to sleep, he understood. "You want I should take you to the toilet?" Nonsense, Mama said. There was a chamber pot in my room, no need to go outside in zero weather. But Papa knew how the pot offended my dignity. Kneeling by the bed he buckled on my galoshes, tumbled me into my coat and tied the knitted cap under my chin. Then out into the frosty night, feet crunching on the fresh snow. I always left the door of the privy open. That way I could look out at the silhouettes of pine trees, dark under the northern lights, and hear the distant yapping of coyotes. Papa stood comfortably close, rolling and crushing in his hands the tissue wrappings saved from crates of oranges. Most people had to use newspaper or pages torn from old catalogues.

In the store, he tried to enforce Mama's rule against eating between meals, but the desire to give pleasure overcame scruple. "A fresh fig bar?" he would ask. Or, "Look, this is a new kind!" (breaking open a chocolate marshmallow puff to reveal, at its quaking center, a jelly heart). Though he had never learned to say NO, he hesitated a little the day I asked for a second box of popcorn. "What would Mama say? So much sweet an hour before supper-time?"

"But, Papa—" I gave his hand a conspiratorial squeeze. "I won't even eat it. I just want the prize."

"Friedele, you want another kewpie, we get one from the toys. No need to open popcorn."

"But I didn't want this kewpie doll! Hazel got a ring with a rubber bulb and it squirts water." I put my arms around his neck. "Please, Papa, I want a ring."

"All right. We try another box." He spilled the popcorn onto the counter. A tin whistle rolled out.

"Oh, I wanted a ring!"

"Now then, we try one more, just one."

But the next box produced a mirror, the one after that a toy compass. It became a game. Papa slit open the tops of the boxes, I shook out the popcorn. And that was how Mama found us when she came to say supper was burned already—Papa busy with the broom and I on the counter, queen of the popcorn mountain.

My mother, in memory, is always moving, blurring the camera image with swift energy. Baskets of clothes to the line, wax on the floors, blintzes in the pan, ruffles spinning out under the sewing machine needle. . . . My father is a still picture. At the store, he sits on a high stool, copying out accounts (mostly uncollectable) in his elegant embellished script, or leans over the counter talking. At home, the chair and the book. One moment I remember especially, a spring scene. Exhilarated by the first mild days of May, with maples dropping pink tassels and the world greening over, I am dashing off to school bare-legged and bare-

armed. Papa cautions, "Take a coat, dear heart. I see clouds."
"It won't rain!" I call over my shoulder. An hour later,
during arithmetic class, the storm breaks. Shivering, I watch
hail pellets bounce off roofs and slatted sidewalks. How will
I get home in my organdy dress, my taffeta hair bow?
(Most children eat lard pail lunches, but Mama likes us
to have hot meals at noon.) I think of tapioca pudding. . . .
Maybe knishes with sour cream. . . . I will have to make
do with my recess apple. I stare miserably out the window,
careless now of multiplication tables. And then I see my
father. He has left the store, in the middle of a business
day, and stands there motionless, waiting, holding high his
black silk unbrella.

My mother acted, my father thought. My mother talked,
my father read. *Der Tog,* the Jewish newspaper from New
York, copies long outdated by the time they reached us
in Birch Hills; the Talmud and its many commentaries; the
stories of Sholem Aleichem. Often he laid aside the book to
share a folk tale that delighted him. "A *yolde,* a foolish
fellow, wishes to go courting. But he has no words. 'Papa,'
he asks, 'what shall I say?' 'Easy,' says the father. 'First,
you discuss love. Then, family. And afterwards, a little
philosophy.' The son goes, happy, but ten minutes later
he is back. "What happened?' asks the father. 'You didn't
do like I told you?' 'I did,' says the *yolde.* 'First, love. I
said, "Do you like noodles?" and she said, "Yes." Then,
family. "Do you have a brother?" She said, "No." That left
only philosophy. So I asked her, I said, "Well, if you did
have a brother, *would* he like noodles?"'"

I did not much enjoy Papa's Jewish stories. The landscape was unfamiliar, a world peopled by rabbis, starving
melameds (teachers), matchmakers, grandfathers with ear-

locks and long caftans. Their concerns, too, were utterly foreign. What to me was the concept of *derech-eretz*, respect to parents, on which so many punch lines depended? Or *yikhus*, honor, an abstraction passionately sought by these bizarre characters? Perhaps only an Eastern European Jew, accustomed to the fantastic intricacies of Talmudic interpretation, could have appreciated the logic-chopping of these folk tale heroes. (I recall happily, however, simpler thrusts of logic. Like the story of the two guests whose hostess offers, at tea, a plate with two *kichlach*, egg cookies. One cookie is a touch bigger than the other. The Jews eye the plate. "You first," says Jacob. "No, you," says Isaac. So Jacob takes—the larger *kichl*. Isaac is indignant. "How come a Jew has no manners? You took the big one!" "And if you had been first, what would you have done?" Jacob inquires mildly. "I would have taken the smaller!" says Isaac. "Then," says Jacob, "why do you complain? *You have it!*") The life pattern which alone could have made these tales comprehensible was mysterious to me. My father would laugh delightedly at the story of the Jewish six-year-old reproved, by a passing elder, for playing in the street barefoot and without trousers. "Why are you not in school?" asks the elder. "Because yesterday I got married," says the boy. "A married man and no trousers?" The sage is scandalized. "Well," says the boy, "yesterday I got married, I wore the trousers. Today my brother gets married, *he* wears the trousers!" "But why is the boy married?" I would ask. I could not read, in my father's warm brown eyes, the poverty of the ghetto Jews, their desperate stratagems to save children from the Czar's Army.

"It's nothing. Just a foolishness." He would have liked to pass on the heritage of Judaism, only without its harsh, fearful knowledges—as if there could be a Passover *seder* without *maroses*, bitter herbs. And then he would tell me another story about Goodie and Baddie. Sitting in his lap, my head against the blue shirt that smelled like sunshine and flatiron steam, I surrendered again to the comforting predictableness of these heroines. Goodie was just like me —she had curly hair, loved her Mama and Papa, and did as she was told. Baddie was always going into the dark forest, where her Mama had distinctly forbidden her to go. I pictured her as having straight hair like my sister's. Dragons, giants, elves, monsters, wicked kings . . . they were all vanquished by bedtime, and Baddie turned good. In my sophisticated twenties I recalled these stories, with their Manichean dualism, as evidence of my father's simplicity. I have wondered, since, whether his understanding was not more complex than it seemed. Was I not Baddie too?

I see my father in the context of domestic life. The friendliest of men, he had no friends but us. Would it have been different in the city, in a Jewish community? I don't know. But certainly, marooned on the prairies, an island of Jewishness in a barbarian sea, he never formed ties beyond the limits of his business life. In the store he was sociable, and on a variety of levels. He talked crops with farmers, theology with the local minister, household matters with women. But he would no more have thought of accompanying a farmer to the beer parlor than, years before, he could have joined a Cossack for a gallop across the steppes. The feeling was not snobbishness in the sense of "I am better than you" or "My position is above yours." It was a pride without vanity, the exclusiveness of the *shtetl* Jew who has learned to say, of walls or barbed wire, "Fences keep them out. They do not keep me in."

Though money and social position played no part in Papa's ambitions for his children, he shared the traditional Jewish concern with *naches*. It is difficult to translate into English this elusive term. *Naches* is pride, but pride in spiritual or intellectual attainments, and so illuminated with loving joy. *Naches* accrued when my sister played in the piano festival, when I won a scholarship to the university. Papa's first happiness in my academic honors, however, was modified by a growing anxiety. A B.A. was fine, splendid, qualifying me, in the marriage market, for a world of Jewish doctors and lawyers. An M.A.—probably all right still. A doctor likes an educated wife. The Ph.D., however, gave him pause. "With a Ph.D., you don't marry just an ordinary intelligent person. So how many Yiddishe boys have a Ph.D.?" Learning and family life, those two great primary goals, warred in him now. *"Freidele zoll kennen lernen Torah. . . ."* What if the studies he had urged should, in the end, destroy my Jewishness?

I think he was not surprised when I told him I had fallen in love with a gentile. Devastated, but not surprised. The curse of the evil eye awaits those whose happiness is too great. (Had he not told me how, in the old country, women covered the faces of infants lest general admiration invite disaster?) And so there began the passionate, unequal struggle. I was young, confident, a city intellectual certified by the university; my father was a failed painter, an unsuccessful country merchant. Such authority as he might have exercised he had abrogated willingly years back. ("A wise head," he used to say, introducing me to strangers. "Nine years old, already she knows more than her Papa.") He was like the unwary knight who, pursuing a quest, relinquishes one after another his sword, his lance, his shield, only to find he stands defenseless when the dragon roars. My father did not argue or threaten. (I had known girls who, after marriage to a gentile, were pronounced officially dead. Their families sat *shiva*, in ritual mourning for the departed.) Papa's response was characteristic. He invoked my mother—"This kills her"—and he told stories. Now, for the first time, I heard tales of pogroms. "Every gentile is a barbarian at heart," he would say. "I know. In Russia we had friends, peasants, drank tea in our kitchen daily. When the Cossacks came, they took sticks and guns, these friends, and fell upon the Jews. One, a neighbor, dragged from a cart a young Jewish woman, was nursing a child. The woman he took by force on the dirt of the barnyard. And when the child cried— I saw with my own eyes, I lay hidden in my father's granary—the child he struck on the head with a stone, and threw to his pigs. Three days later, when the Czar said, 'Enough,' back comes this *goy* to our kitchen. For tea." When he saw I was not to be moved, he wrote me a letter. "Once upon a time," he began, "there lived a young man, a scholar and a good son. And it came to pass that he fell in love with a beautiful girl. Now this girl was a witch. Flowers, fruits, jewels he brought to her, and still she refused him. 'What can I do,' he cried, 'that you should love me?' The witch smiled and said, 'Bring me your mother's heart.' Now this young man's mother was dear to him. But he was in love. He took a knife and cut out his mother's heart and ran with it, still warm and bleeding, to the witch. In such a hurry, he tripped and fell. The heart slipped from his hand. He was frightened. His gift, maybe, spoiled? But as he picked it up, the heart spoke. "O my dear son, I hope you have not hurt yourself."

My marriage did not kill my mother; she was made of sterner stuff. A pragmatist, she started from the premise given. It placed my father, however, in an extraordinary position. Central to his whole being were the principles that his child could do no wrong, and for a Jew to marry a gentile was wrong. Even God cannot will a contradiction; my father was forced to rise above the shuddering clash of axioms. He did so, not by feats of casuistry, but by a kind of gentle distancing. He became no less loving, but more remote. Perhaps we had never talked seriously after I moved into the university world and a set of heterodox opinions. Now, when I came home for visits, we spoke only of domestic matters. His fears—and they must have been many—appeared only incidentally, as when, observing that I walked barefoot in summer, he said, "But when you go to bed, you wash well the feet, yes?" I laughed. "My husband doesn't check my feet." Papa looked grave. "*Now* he doesn't. But an old wife with dirty feet, this is another matter. You remember that story, the Jew who complains, 'I married a young *shiksa*, now I have an old *goy*?'" A *shiksa* is a nubile stranger, sensual and passionate; the *goy* is the enemy. Did his imagination leap ahead to those classic scenes in which the husband calls his wife *dirty Jew*? Or the children turn anti-Semite and forswear their mother?

Always a demonstrative man, my father embraced me very seldom after I married. In this new reserve, there lay no hint of reproach. I remained his own dear child. Whatever had gone wrong, the fault must be his. If he had given me a proper Jewish education . . . if we had faithfully kept the Sabbath . . . if he had taken us earlier to the city, to be among our own kind. . . . He sighed heavily, reading the paper, and I would look up from my book. "What's the matter, Papa?" "It says here that Ted Williams, a baseball player, makes for the year fifty thousand dollars. And my daughter, a college graduate, scholarships and medals you can't count them, gets twenty-five hundred." "That was last year, Papa. Now that I'm not teaching, I get seventy-five cents an hour marking papers." Given at last a suitable target, he raged. "What kind of a world? Where is justice, where? An ignoramus with a baseball bat —and Gelber's daughter, a nothing, a head a potato, is engaged I hear a Jewish professor!"

"Annie Gelber's not stupid, Pa." I tried tactful diversion. "She's at the university this year. Do you know what she's taking?"

"Taking?" A melancholy smile. "Sandwiches, that's what she's taking!" He looked at me, eyes full of tears at the thought of the Jewish professor who would never marry me now. Then, very quietly, "I don't want you should mark papers for seventy-five cents an hour. I give you a dollar an hour *not* to mark them."

One morning, opening a jar of raspberry jam I had made the summer before—the last summer I carried his dreams— he stood scraping a delicate fingernail on the paraffin seal.

"Has it gone moldy?" I asked.

He held the wax wafer to the light and I saw, stuck to the underside, a strand of black hair.

"I'm sorry. I should wear hair nets when I cook. Let me fix that."

But he had deftly disengaged the single hair. He walked to the dining room china cabinet and unlocked it. All that visit I saw my hair in the crystal candy dish. It was not a ritual burial; my father loved my life. No, it was rather a ceremonial guard, behind the cabinet's glass doors, of Sleeping Beauty. The prophecy had been fulfilled, the wicked fairy had struck, and all the joy of the household had sunk into heavy sleep while thorns tangled the palace gates. But who was to say that the future might not still be bright and that somehow, triumphing over appearances, the prince might not yet come?

World War II did for my father what no amount of industry had ever accomplished; it gave him a measure of success. Wages rose and job openings multiplied, farmers grew rich, and money flowed into small towns hungry for decades. Goods were scarce. A merchant with a substantial stock was bound to prosper. Papa repriced his pre-war woolens, observing, as he changed "2's" to "3's," "You see, it is not lost, that training from the art school. I make at last money with my pencil." Faces not seen in years reappeared at the grocery counter. "You got sugar, Bruser? Raisins?" Papa reported wryly new developments in the human comedy. "Guess who comes back today? Mrs. Dreyba, has had here a bill from three Christmases back and passed by the store like a blind woman. Now she tells me Johnson is no good, keeps the dried apples for special customers. I sold her a tin strawberry jam and she says, 'You're a real white man, Bruser.' Such friends are good to have."

Papa took on another clerk, had the store painted, met his bills on time. But these evidences of financial security did not delight him. He moved more slowly. Talking to customers, he seemed the aging actor in a long-run play, a man who, having wearied of the role, produces lines and gestures he can no longer feel. His manner with children, even, suggested an edgy impatience, the orange given not so much affectionately as to keep the child quiet so he might conclude the transaction, get back to the house, and rest. "He falls asleep all the time," I reported on a summer visit to Grandview. "I've seen him sit down at the store desk and suddenly drop off." "He's tired," Mama said. "Overworked." He returned from a buying trip to Winnipeg with an alarming tale, presented as a joke. He had fallen in the street—"I don't know what happens, all of a sudden I'm dizzy, I go down like a stone"—and been picked up by the police as a drunk. A doctor, consulted hastily, said, "Inner ear disturbance. Nothing serious." But the sky darkened. He would forget to lock up, mislay the bank book. One evening, after a particularly brisk Saturday, he asked, "Where's the money?" "In the register?" Mama said. It wasn't there. We looked in drawers and on tables. "Think, Boris," Mama urged. "Where did you put it? The register tape shows over five hundred dollars we took in." Papa shielded his eyes with his hand. In the last few months dull red blotches had spread over his white indoor skin. "I don't know," he said. "I remember nothing. Nothing." We found the money, neatly rolled, in the rice bin. It was decided: the store must be sold.

In forty years of marriage, my parents had never taken a holiday together. They had never taken holidays at all, only traveled separately to see relations or conduct business. Now, with the store sold, my mother laid plans. What does a Jewish storekeeper do when he retires? In the old country he would have bought his wife a Sabbath dress and pearls. In the new world he buys her a fur coat and goes to Florida. My mother frowned over the coat, but that was clearly a part of the ritual, evidence to the world that Boris Bruser had made the grade at last. We saw them off in a scene like a stage set, or a travel agent's folder: Mama flushed and overheated in her mink jacket, bought wholesale; Papa in a straw hat and two-color suede oxfords. Mama sent us accordion-pleated postcards (flamingoes, cabanas, tropical foliage, hotel lounge) and then, two weeks after their arrival in Miami, a telegram. My father had been struck by an out-of-control car that veered onto the traffic island where he stood awaiting a red light.

If it is true that life approximates to the condition of art, then Papa's was the perfect life—unified, consistent, whole. Lying on his hospital bed, with two broken legs and a compound skull fracture, he repeated wonderingly, "But I am standing the whole time on the safety island." The negligent driver was penniless and uninsured. Medical bills poured in—often from totally unfamiliar doctors who claimed to have been consulted, or present at the accident site. Six months in that Florida hospital consumed a decade's savings; he came home on crutches and was never well again. Mama wept, "Where is justice?" but Papa shrugged. He stood with Tevyeh the dairyman: "The Lord is good to all—and suppose He forgets somebody now and again, good Lord, hasn't He enough on his mind?"

My father's last illness came slowly on. There was never a moment on which you could place your finger, saying, "He has lost touch," never a clear line crossed. Retired, settled now in Winnipeg, he simply became quieter, less mobile. ("It is the accident," we said to each other. "His legs hurt.") He read for longer periods, turning the pages a little too slowly—but he never held a book upside down. His emotions, always easily touched, were triggered now by cruder stimuli. He would weep, sitting before the television. "How can you get worked up over such trash?" I would say, snapping the channels. I was impatient, too, when he asked once again for my sister's address. Hadn't he written to her, to the same house in Toronto, for twenty years? "She lives in Alaska," I would say. Or "Timbuctu." He smiled. "This I know. But in Timbuctu *what street?*" Only occasionally I felt a leap of fear. He would look out the window, freshly interested and then puzzled. "When did they build so many new houses? Already you can't see the grain elevators." "Papa!" (Keep it steady, don't frighten him.) "You're in Winnipeg, not Grandview!" And he was my familiar father again, motioning away the foolishness with a wave of his hand. "Of course, I know. I was asleep a little minute, and waking I forgot." His paths contracted. Stairs were an effort, streets treacherous. Now he scuffed the rug in a cautious trek from bed to bathroom to chair. I would have thought him helpless, except that sometimes, when Mama and I went out for a walk around the block, someone had made it to the kitchen with remarkable speed and cleaned out the cookie jar. Questioned, he shook his head. "Reading the whole time. Mice, maybe." Though the doctor recommended a strict diet, I urged indulgence. Surely, in a shrinking life, he might enjoy the pleasures of pastry? "He is too heavy," Mama said. "If he falls, who will lift him?"

There is a special sadness that comes with reversal of roles in the life between parent and child—when the child literally becomes father of the man. I grew accustomed to that sorrow. Still I cannot think without pain of the day I bathed my father. It was such a logical task to assume; my mother had trouble with her shoulder, I was younger and stronger. But I had always temporized. "I'll put dinner on while you bathe Papa." This time, Mama ill with a headache, the apartment hot and steamy, I took his arm and persuaded him to the tub. He had been silent for days; he did not speak as I fumbled with buttons and zipper, easing him out of his clothes. I knew the procedure. "Here—feet on the rubber mat, so you don't slip. Now, hang on to the shower curtain bar. Both hands."

When I was a child, I often tried to see my father naked. I remember hanging about the kitchen door on bath nights, but for all his earthiness he was careful about that. It was no good, now, trying not to look. His skin was whiter than I would have believed possible, and strangely smooth—the skin of a man who has lived indoors and never used his body except for love. Even now, in age, his sex hung enormous. I remembered his telling us, years ago, how women had admired him. Why, a prostitute, with all *her* experience, said she had never encountered a man so magnificently endowed. Standing awkwardly crouched in the tub—he was too tall for this arrangement— my father met my eyes. He began to stutter, as he did, sometimes, in the days when he had speech and grew excited. "T-t-t-t-t. . . ." "What is it, Papa?" He shook his head, frustrated, and I saw that he was crying, but then the cry became a laugh, a strange hysterical mirth that filled the small room with its shrill despair. "I shouldn't bathe him," I said to my mother, leading him, terry-robed, back to the chair. "It's humiliating." "Does he know?" she asked. "He just doesn't like baths." I knew she was wrong. Drifted away he was, lost and confused and wandering, but that brief indignity had summoned him back to protest. A woman does not look upon her father's nakedness.

It does not seem to me that we ever *decided* to move my father to a nursing home—only that a current carried us towards that sad inevitability. In the process of *not* considering, we exchanged cheerless assurances of progress —at least, of holding ground. "Yesterday he recognized Weintraub," my mother would say. "Think of it—a man he hasn't seen for twenty years." (But of course we all knew that the shreds of memory clung, like smoke, to a distant landscape. It was now, ten minutes ago, last week, that escaped him.) "We had a long discussion about Uncle Colman," my sister said. "Dad said Colman was a wonderful fellow, a prince." (I had heard that discussion. Cecely talked, my father listened with soft, unfocused gaze. And when she prodded, "Don't you think so, Dad? Isn't Colman a prince?" Papa said, "Yes.") Reality was the frightening difficulty of moving a large man whose limbs no longer seemed part of him. "Right now," the social worker said, "you could still get him into one of the better places. I mean, Mr. Bruser looks pretty good, and he's got some control. Later on—well, have you seen the King Edward?"

We had seen the King Edward Hospital for Incurables. We found a nursing home. My father wore his best suit for the journey (by ambulance; he had difficulty getting in and out of cars), and he did indeed look good. He said not a word the whole time. A nurse flicked a cold eye over his possessions. "You can take back the pajama bottoms," she said. And then, looking at his old chinchilla coat, which Mama had cleaned and brushed that morning, "He won't need *that* again." We stayed just until supper was served ("We feed them at four, that way they're ready for bed by seven"), and my father spoke at last. Supper was mashed potatoes, unnaturally loose and milky, with a slice of plastic-foam bread, a thick pool of gravy, and sausages. Papa had told me, once, how the Czar dragooned

Jewish boys into his Army and defiled them with pork. Now he took up his fork. *"Wait for Sabbath bread and you lose the plain."* My mother moved away so that he should not see her face, and he startled a minute. "Where is Mama going?" "Shopping," I said. "Eaton's has a sale."

I saw my father only summers, when I made the long trip from New Hampshire to Winnipeg. The surprising thing was that, on the surface, the changes were so slight. Seated in his wheelchair or propped on pillows, he remained a handsome man, his face unlined, his hair still dark at the roots. "He looks younger than I do," my mother sighed. "He has no worries." Increasingly, though, there were two faces: my father's, and that of a dull-eyed stranger, slack-jawed, unstrung. He was almost always able to summon himself for the moment of greeting. (Names would not come to him, only, "Hello, *dear.*") Then he would begin to drift. Normal conversation being impossible, we devised a game, the kind of quiz one gives children to explore their skills. "What's my name, Papa?" He waved this one away. Impossible to tell whether he had forgotten, or merely felt the query demeaning, ridiculous. One day, when he had not spoken at all, I teased him with questions. "What do I do, Papa? Am I a musician?"

Silence.

"Am I a dentist?"

A smile. Whatever I might be, I was not that.

"A lawyer?" He shook his head. "A nurse? An engineer? A teacher?" He hesitated, then frowned *No.* "A doctor, a scientist, a judge. . . ."

He spoke suddenly with absolute clarity. "I know, dear, whatever you do, you do *well.*"

He kept now strange company. The room, technically semiprivate, accommodated three other beds, and through those beds moved a lamentable procession of the helpless and senile. A legless man with the unnerving habit of removing his prosthetic legs when he had climbed into a wheelchair; a profane French Canadian who filled the room with bilingual obscenities; old men who fought and complained and wept and emptied their bowels freely. . . . My father stared them all down. He seemed unaware of the others until a more than ordinary disturbance attracted his attention and then, looking very much like De Gaulle confronting his critics, he would ask, "Who is that hooli*gan?*" (He pronounced this word Russian style, with accent on the final syllable.) Something invincibly aristocratic shaped his features till the end; the orderlies who addressed him in familiar style—"Eat up now, Ben, that's a good boy!"—seemed merely absurd, the bumpkins of *Midsummer Night's Dream* transported onto the wind-swept heath of *Lear*.

The last time I saw my father he lay high on pillows under a white sheet. (The nurses had given up dressing or moving him into a chair. Windows and doors all one to him now.) His mouth hung partly open, revealing the smooth gums. (He had eaten away his teeth, and how could he be fitted for dentures?) His eyes were filmed with the haze of advanced glaucoma and his arms, outlined under the cover, lay straight at his sides, as if arranged by someone else. He looked at me without change of expression. "Papa," I whispered, "it's me." Then, using the name he called me when I was little, "It's Freidele." I felt, as if it were a physical thing, the slow tremendous effort to gather himself together. Intelligence and recollection gradually suffused his face, the way light flushes through a neon tube. "Freidele," he re-

peated wonderingly. "Dear child." He drew one hand out
from under the sheet and placed it, palm down, on mine.

I had always admired his beautiful hands. Mine are
stubby-fingered, suggesting a certain peasant coarseness; he
had long, delicate fingers with oval nails, crescent-mooned
—the hands of a Bronzino portrait. That day a brown stain
showed under the nails. He watched as I scrubbed with a
soapy cloth. "Am I hurting you, Papa?" "No, dear, how could
you hurt me?" A last ambiguity from a most unambiguous
man.

I learned from a stranger that my father was dying. Three
thousand miles away a voice said, "If you want to see your
father alive, come at once." I packed slowly, without tears,
and on the plane I had a long conversation with a Saskatchewan farmer about new methods of grain production. I worried about not being able to cry at the funeral. How could I
explain that his passing was a relief, that I had been waiting
for death to give me back my father?

To know what one really feels is a lifetime's learning. It
seemed to me, leaving for the funeral, that the day's cere-
mony merely recognized what had occurred years before.
Why then be upset? And indeed, I could have protected myself against anything said in English, for English is the language of my rational life. How could I know the *shamas*
would ask me, before the service, to repeat a Hebrew prayer?
"*Boruch atoy adenoy elohenu,* Blessed art thou, O Lord
our God, King of the Universe. . . ." I learned it on a summer afternoon forty years ago, the day I came home crying
after boys called me a kike. "They make fun out of bitterness," Papa said, stroking my hair. "Because God has chosen
the Jews, from all nations in the earth." *Boruch atoy adenoy
elohenu,* my father chanting *kiddush* over the winking wine

. . . my father telling me how Moses led his people out of
bondage in Egypt, the Lord before them by day in a pillar
of cloud, by night in a pillar of fire ("And Moses stretched
out his hand over the sea, and the Lord . . . made the sea
dry land, and the waters were divided.") Passover matzo,
the heavy-sweet *hamantashen* of Purim bursting with honey
and poppy seeds, green boughs at Sukkos and the dizzy-
spinning *dreydel* at Hanukkah. . . . *Boruch atoy,* the surprise of my temperate father wine-flushed at the *seder,* singing our favorite song, *Chad Gadyoh,* and then the always
stunning stroke by which a familiar nursery-rhyme pattern
("Then came a dog and bit the cat that ate the kid . . . !")
was transformed into a shout of triumph, the ancient Hebrew ecstasy: "Then came the Holy One, blessed be He, and
slew the angel of death that took the butcher that killed the
ox that drank the water that quenched the fire that burnt
the stick that beat the dog that bit the cat that ate the kid
My father bought for two *zuzim!*"

At the cemetery, six young men who had never known my
father carried the coffin to the grave's edge. The rabbi stood
there under a canopy, hunching into his upturned coat collar.
(Was it the same *chupah* that arches over a bride and
groom?) A mat of artificial grass, like the straw lining Easter
baskets, lay rolled to one side, ready. The rabbi approached,
blinking rain from his glasses. "Will you say *Kaddish* for your
father?" he asked. "I can't," I said. "I don't know how." As
he turned away, a wild gust of wet wind tore at my um-
brella, straining the bright shaft.

Father, I write your name in tears: Dov Ber, the son of
Chaim.

FROM YON FAR COUNTRY

Into my heart an air that kills
From yon far country blows:
What are those blue remembered hills,
What spires, what farms are those?

THEY ARE NOT all happy highways where I went. What, then, drives me down them again, after all these years and another life? The effort, I suppose, to understand. Somewhere, in yon far country, lies the answer to the question that confronts me with increasing urgency. Who am I?

I begin with the simplest things. I was born a woman in a family where women were valued. Years later, encounters with the expectant father of popular mythology—craving a son to complete his manhood—astonished me. So too did the discovery that many girls felt themselves, by reason of sex alone, disappointing to their parents. I never doubted that mine preferred girls. In my mother, partiality was perhaps a reaction to the circumstances of her own childhood. She had grown up in a household where boys were kings and girls scullery maids. How I shuddered, as a child, at the tales of my grandmother, cruel as any legendary stepmother, making strawberry jam for her sons and allowing her daughters only a taste of the floating pink scum from the pot. More dreadful was the story of a crisis that occurred

during the family's emigration to Canada. They had left
Russia with their gold, literally, in their teeth, sacks of dried
cherries for the journey, and five children. In London my
grandmother became ill—too ill, she decided, to care for
her sickly youngest girl, an infant in arms. "Anyway she will
die," this extraordinary woman announced. "So we leave
her here, in the railway station. It is easier then for us all."
Lucy was not left behind; my mother, nine years old,
strapped the baby to her back and carried her throughout
the long ocean voyage. My mother never spoke of her own
upbringing except with awe, the Jew's *derech-eretz*, and a
muted regret for love never received. But the experience
marked her, and when she acquired daughters of her own,
she redressed the balance with a fierce protective joy. She
made us queens—and my father paid homage. In him the
feeling for women had always, I think, a strongly sexual element. He would have enthusiastically endorsed Robert
Burns' view: "[God's] 'prentice han he tried on man And
then he made the lasses, oh!" And indeed, now that I
think of it, his delight in femaleness had just Burns' combination of energy and bawdy humor. He really liked girls,
and, though a notably faithful husband, he never lost his
connoisseur's eye. "She burns under her dress," he would
say of a particularly lusty wench. Even when I was little,
that remark told me something about my father, too. In a
quite innocent and unselfconscious way, he treated us as
sexual persons—future mothers, future brides. Being a
woman, I knew, was a privilege. Women were *special*.

The fact that I was also a Jew reinforced this sense of
uniqueness. Of course there were disadvantages. Many
times, during my lonely childhood, I would have sold my
birthright for a mess of pottage—but the chance never came.

Every Jewish child has heard, in his heart's core, the cry Victor Hugo puts in the mouth of a tormented Moses: "*Laissez-moi m'endormir le sommeil de la terre!*" But when the common sleep of earth is denied, one learns to profit from the mixed blessing of eternal wakefulness. Being different anyway, the Jew must actively embrace and cultivate his difference; this theme ran through all my parents' injunctions. "It is not enough a Jew should be good," my father used to say. "He has to be *best*." Not in everything, to be sure. Certain areas, like physical prowess, were un-Jewish; distinction here was meaningless, if not downright reprehensible. (My father told us once how, as a boy, he longed for a ball. He knew better than to ask Grandpa, but every day, when no one was watching, he would creep out to the stable, where the family horse was kept, and run his hand back and forth over the animal's back. In this way he acquired, gradually, a small springy coil of hair. At last— it took almost a year—the ball was the right size. He had given it just one good bounce when my grandfather appeared, outraged and incredulous. "Shame on you!" The old man snatched the ball and flung it into the pigpen. "You have no pride? That my son should make sport—*like a gentile!*")

In character, conduct, and intellectual pursuits, however, the Jew had an obligation to shine. For years I was driven, through school and then university, by a wild competitive urge—to get the highest marks, gather up all the prizes, and lay them at my parents' feet. It was a kind of madness. (Still, in dreams, I see myself called to take examinations for which I am not ready, and I wake sweating.) Blind, selfish, destructive . . . it was all these things. I took mathematics, which I hated, rather than the literature I loved, because math courses offered the best chance of a perfect score. I studied fifteen, eighteen hours a day, much of the time devoted to pure memorization. (One year I committed to memory the whole of *Silas Marner* so that I might embellish my exam paper with appropriate quotations.) At the height of the frenzy, I would not only have botanized on my grandmother's grave, I would have dug it up, if necessary, to ensure a scholastic triumph. And yet—such is the ambiguity of most gifts—the same forces which drove me to run faster plagued me with uneasy questions. *Why* was I running? And where? Bred in a tradition of respect for truth, because I was a Jew, I stopped at last to think.

Jewishness conferred upon me other gifts. Experiencing very young the effects of ignorant prejudice, I was made incapable of inflicting that particular savagery upon others. Aversion to violence, drunkenness, demagoguery—anything against reason—all this I acquired by osmosis. Also, in strange ways, I came to see my life as having significance beyond its obvious narrow limits. I was not just Freidele Bruser, the youngest child of a country merchant, but an actor in the cosmic drama that included Abraham and Isaac, David and Solomon and Daniel and Job. Scientists, scholars, philosophers, makers of music, my people had for centuries brooded on the burthen of the mystery and, sometimes, seen into the life of things. Einstein's conquest of space, Bergson's of time, and Freud's of the dark unconscious—these were my triumphs too.

Woman and Jew, I am also my parents' child. Inescapably. Had I been given a choice, I might have chosen different qualities to inherit. (How I sighed, growing up, for my father's narrow hips and my mother's face! Later I reflected sadly on other gifts not given—but one must learn, in Maslow's phrase, to love one's fate.) Biologically, my father seems to have transmitted very little to me; it was my sister who inherited his physical grace and, perhaps, a certain incapacity for coping with the real world. I never felt *like* my father. I admired without desire to emulate, and yet his clear nobility provided a standard of value in my life. My mother's influence was overwhelming. I had only to look in the mirror to see that I too was a Slobinsky, the very name suggestive of the build. (It has taken me many years to value the rugged constitution which went along with a thickness of waist and ankle.) By blood or example, I acquired early my mother's need to be busy, to take charge. From her, too, came a need to achieve stability (or its illusion) in a world of change. Wherever we moved, she planted a garden. The most unpromising circumstances overnight became home. This wizardry she achieved, in part, symbolically. A Boston fern in a sunny window; bright embroidered pillows plumped on the sofa; a silver samovar; the lace bedspread laid over pink taffeta. . . . These assurances triumphed over dirt floors and outdoor toilets. Though my mother abandoned the elaborate domestic rituals of Jewish orthodoxy, a certain feeling for ritual remained—not worship the Lord in the beauty of holiness, but worship life in the beauty of order. There were no snacks eaten standing in our house. Even breakfast was a proper meal, with the table set and napkins rolled in silver rings beside glasses of freshly squeezed orange juice. Milk waited in a pitcher, jelly in crystal. While I never shared my sister's bright conviction that our family had secret reserves of wealth, I understood how she got the notion. Without money, we lived rich.

Though my parents rarely talked about such things, it

would have been hard to grow up during the twenties and thirties without knowing money was scarce. The Depression stamped me. I still cannot make a purchase without moves to ascertain that I am paying the lowest possible price. I cannot throw out food. My closets bulge with out-of-fashion garments no one would wear. And yet, I think, the fabric is still good. I might make them over, cut them up for rugs. . . . From a thousand penny-pinched situations I breathed in frugality. Prune pits yield a nut only slightly bitterer than almonds; souring milk hung in bags on the line turns into a fine cheese; roadside gleanings (choke-cherries, saskatoons, rose hips) make a jam superior to that of many orchard fruits. (We had peach or apricot preserves only when crates of ripe fruit in my father's store remained unsold on Saturday night. In that case my mother would be bustling about early Sunday morning with hot jars and paraffin.)

Invaluable training as a shopper came during the years when my mother, my sister, and I lived in a Winnipeg apartment while, in a remote Manitoba village, my father battled insolvency and tried to undersell the T. Eaton Co. No small-scale merchant, buying at normal wholesale, could meet the prices listed in Eaton's catalogue. The solution, oddly enough, was to buy at Eaton's retail store, on sale. Almost daily, during the lean years, Eaton's Winnipeg branch offered "loss leaders" at incredible prices. (Saturday mornings the five-cent special was particularly good, but for that you might wait hours in line.) My job was to walk to school the long way round, stopping in at Eaton's to shop. Outside the store before the eight-thirty opening, I would join the crush of early-bird shoppers leaning on the plush ropes awaiting the gong. When that sounded, I raced for the stairs. All the best buys were in the basement—and I had discovered that waiting for elevators reduced one's lead by precious seconds. Breathless, I scooped up the day's specials, which might include ladies' hats for twenty cents or seven cans of tomatoes for a quarter. Then, laden with packages, I staggered upstairs to the free check room, where the bundles could be picked up on my return from school. Weekends, my father came in from the country and returned by bus, lugging his cut-rate stock. Except for those occasions when suspicious clerks questioned me (Eaton's policy forbade quantity sales to jobbers) I quite enjoyed my adventures in commerce. To this day, a really good special stirs my heart like a trumpet. "Men's merino combinations, ninety-nine cents" I will read from the discount store ad. My husband, absorbed in higher matters, frowns. "What on earth do you want with merino combinations?" I am already figuring the profit per dozen at normal resale prices.

Even stronger than the effect of the economic scene was the prairie landscape. We are all marked by the first world that meets our eyes, carrying it with us as a permanent image of the way things are, or should be. My world was flat and open. There were no "prospects" on the prairies—only one prospect, the absolute, uncompromising monotony of those two parallel infinities, earth and sky. I draw it, in my mind's eye, with a ruler—road and tree, farmhouse and elevator, all spare and simple and hard-edged, with a line of telephone poles slicing the distance. Movement in this landscape has no more consequence than the leap of a jackrabbit across a dusty road. The stillness is the reality. The sounds of the prairie only deepen its loneliness—cowbells clinking in the dusk, the curious thrilling hum of telephone wires, a coyote's yelp. Sometimes at night we heard the long low whistle of a train, saw the lighted snake as it rushed out of one mystery into another. Faces at the windows, dining car napery. . . . Its passing left us more solitary than ever. To grow up on the prairies is to acquire inevitably the image of man as a lone traveler, moving through a universe neither hostile nor friendly but only infinitely remote. The sky does not shelter, the trees do not shade. Even flowers keep their distance. I think of rough black-eyed Susans, great patches of them standing in the summer sun, with bristly stems and leaves that tore the fingers; or, another extreme, unbelievably delicate blue-eyed grass, a fairy iris with a minute orange eye that shut when you picked the blossom. As for water—for years it meant only sloughs or rain barrels or, on a grander scale, Lake Winnipeg, whose beaches seemed always infested with fish flies or dead locusts. (Summers, we might crunch fifty feet over loathsome-smelling mounds of insects before the water reached swimming depth.) Trees were small—birches and trembling poplars, swamp willow and yellow-flowered caragana. My primal image of *house,* after years of happier architectural fortunes, is stucco set with chips of colored glass. (A real house has a porch—we called it *veranda*—as midpoint between box shelter and the naked world.) I never think of Saskatchewan as beautiful—British Columbia, in all seasons, offers finer prospects far—and yet its very austerity makes for grandeur. The fall performance of New Brunswick maples, when you come right down to it, seems unduly theatrical; the ocean is too much.

The last significant Canadian influence on my life was, by fine ironic circumstance, a transplanted Anglo-Indian and the son of a Protestant clergyman. I met the man I was to marry at the University of Manitoba, where, through purest accident, he happened to be teaching. British in speech and manner (I had always resented the British, cried when I first read how Wolfe defeated Montcalm on the Plains of Abraham); profoundly Christian in background (he had lost the belief, but temper and vision remained); highly visual as well as verbal, impulsive rather than prudent, committed to the imaginative life beyond all practical considerations—he was obviously unsuitable, so I married him.

Had I deliberately planned to enlarge my experience, I could hardly have done better. My husband introduced me to painting. The Group of Seven revealed the country I had never found in Bliss Carman or Pauline Johnson. Macdonald's churning, hot-colored hills; Jackson's lonely wilderness; Lauren Harris's monolithic world carved out of ice and basalt; Tom Thomson's ragged gallant pines . . . I did not need to know Eastern Canada, or the far West, to recognize the shaping forces here. Chagall set to music my father's Russian stories; Cézanne altered my vision more definitively than my first pair of horn-rimmed glasses. I was a student before I met my husband and a student after—but the spirit of my studies changed. I had known the Talmudic pronouncement that "He who has knowledge, has everything; he who lacks knowledge, lacks everything." My gentile husband communicated the wisdom of a profounder Jewish law: "Make not of the Torah a crown wherewith to glorify thyself nor a spade wherewith to dig."